C000271734

Weathering the Storms

living with epilepsy

Julie Dennison

Emdee
Publishing
EP

In writing this book, I received valuable help from three main sources. The first was the staff at the National Society for Epilepsy who did a great deal of research on my behalf. The second source was the medical staff at the National Hospital for Neurology, in particular Dr Matthew Walker and Professor Michael Trimble who both took an interest in the project and encouraged me to write the book. Also my husband who spent many hours of his time editing and tidying up my words. Finally, the friends who proof read the book and gave me encouragement when I most needed it. Without their help, the book would not have been completed. My thanks go to them all.

Published by Emdee Publishing, Welwyn Garden City, UK

First published 2004

ISBN 0-9546777-0-6

Printed by Black Bear Press, Cambridge, UK

 **ucb Pharma**
committed to epilepsy

Grateful thanks to UCB Pharma for their generous support.

© Julie Dennison, 2004. All rights reserved. No part of this publication may be reproduced, stored in a retrieval system, or transmitted, in any form or by any means, electronic, mechanical, photocopying, recording or otherwise, without the prior written permission of the author (www.livingwithepilepsy.org.uk).

The contents of *Weathering the Storms* are based on many years of personal experience with epilepsy. However, the author is not a medically qualified person. Anyone requiring medical advice should consult a doctor. Whilst the information presented is believed to be correct, the author, the publisher or their agents cannot accept responsibility for any consequences arising from errors or omissions contained in this book.

CONTENTS

FOREWORD

Epilepsy is the commonest serious neurological condition affecting 0.5-1 % of the world's population. In most cases, it is easily controlled by medication, but a significant proportion of people have epilepsy that is resistant to drug treatment. Uncontrolled epilepsy can be a devastating condition. The seizures are usually unpredictable, often occurring at awkward or dangerous times. Not only do people have to suffer the condition, but they have to endure other people's perception of the condition. It is surprising that such prejudice exists, as there have been many prominent people who have had epilepsy such as Tchaikovsky, Alexander the Great, Feodor Dostoevsky, Gustave Flaubert and Vincent van Gogh. Seizures are, however, often frightening to see and we often shy away from what disturbs us.

Julie lectures to schools, epilepsy groups, doctors and nurses, and as a result of these talks and the questions she has been asked, she has written an account of her epilepsy. Julie has severe epilepsy with many attacks a day, yet has led a full life. She has worked, married and built up a family. She has not only faced up to her condition, and, to a large extent, conquered it, but also made others confront their own prejudices. This book contains many lessons for people with and without epilepsy. There is much factual information interspersed with personal experience. Julie's story is striking; a great deal applies not only to epilepsy, but to us all. Perhaps the overwhelming tone of this book is that of optimism, an optimism that I encounter every time I meet Julie, and an optimism that is of benefit to patient and doctor alike.

Matthew Walker
Honorary Consultant and Senior Lecturer in Neurology,
Institute of Neurology, London.

PREFACE

I have had epilepsy throughout my life. It has been disabling but, strangely, an old friend. To have any long term medical condition means having to get used to it, or go downhill with it. One of the ways I came to terms with having epilepsy was to write about it. I wrote articles and gave talks in order to explain my feelings to others, and to reduce ignorance and prejudice of the condition.

My doctor suggested I write a book to explain the different feelings and emotions that I had experienced from my early childhood up to the present day. It took me 16 months of hard work and a lot of time to produce the book, and I have enjoyed writing every bit of it. When I first started, I was afraid that I would only fill a couple of pages about myself. Then I found myself writing about aspects of life with epilepsy that took me quite a while to remember - buried in the depths of my brain.

It is not only the person with epilepsy who suffers, but also the family, friends, colleagues and the ones who try to give support in the only way they know how - by being there. They have been included, as have the doctors and other medical staff without whose help I would be unable to function.

I do hope this book proves to be useful to create awareness of a surprisingly common, but often misunderstood, condition. Readers who have epilepsy themselves may find they experience the same feelings as me. Those who have been spared this affliction, or who have to care for someone with epilepsy, may find it useful to understand what life can be like for those on the 'inside'. The message is ultimately optimistic, that no matter what obstacles a person has to overcome they should get on and enjoy life.

Julie Dennison

Dedicated to my husband, Mike.

1   The facts and the figures first

I find some of the facts about epilepsy quite astonishing. For instance, it is one of the most common neurological conditions and can affect anyone regardless of age, colour or class. There are 300,000 people in the United Kingdom - 40 million world-wide - with active epilepsy.

So, what is epilepsy? It is a disorder of the central nervous system, specifically the brain. Our nervous system is a communications network controlling such things as thoughts, emotions, memory and movement. Our nerves act rather like telephone lines, enabling the brain to communicate with every part of the body using tiny electrical signals. These electrical impulses travel along the network of nerve cells, known as neurons, in the brain and throughout the whole body. They do this by using chemical messengers called neurotransmitters. A seizure occurs when the brain's nerve cells misfire and generate a sudden, uncontrolled surge of electrical activity in the brain. This may be likened to a thunder storm that suddenly releases huge amounts of electrical energy, disrupting our normally ordered lives. Epilepsy is often referred to as a storm in the brain, hence the title of this book.

Epilepsy is not a disease or illness. It is not catching and does not make a person mentally handicapped. Just because you have a seizure (sometimes known as 'a fit') does not mean you have epilepsy. One in twenty people will have a single seizure during their lives. Everyone has the ability to produce a seizure, but in someone with epilepsy it could be that their brain has a low resistance to it. There are different causes, such as brain tumours, scarring on the brain because of head injury or stroke, or even an illness such as meningitis. Epilepsy is ten times more common than multiple sclerosis and as common as diabetes. Four times more people die from sudden unexpected death in epilepsy than die from Aids.

A diagnosis of epilepsy may be made following two or more seizures. There are many different types of epileptic seizure, ranging from the flutter of an eyelid (absence or petit mal) to the well known tonic clonic seizure (or grand mal as it is sometimes called) which can last for several minutes and can appear quite frightening to the onlooker because the sufferer typically falls to the ground making jerking movements, often called convulsions.

Absences are the ones I know particularly well as I experience many every day. These are brief interruptions of consciousness lasting perhaps a few seconds, and I will normally not fall down. When I recover, I may need prompting just to remind me of where I was before the seizure started. This type of seizure is very common in children. However, adults can also suffer from absences and I have many each day. For example, during the time it took to write this paragraph I have had five absence seizures. Because of that, I have had to read this paragraph at least six times to check that it makes sense. This will give you an idea of just how troublesome absence seizures can be, even though they are only small.

There is a seizure called a 'tonic'. In this there is a general stiffening of muscles, without the jerking often known in tonic clonic seizures. There is also the atonic seizure where there is complete loss of muscle tone causing the person to fall. A myoclonic jerk may sound strange but is quite common. It is the abrupt jerking of the limbs and often occurs with other forms of seizure. A simple partial seizure can be the twitching of a limb or a sensation such as a strange taste. The complex partial seizure is quite common. In this, the person may fiddle with buttons or with clothes yet be totally unaware of what is going on around them.

About two to three per cent of people with epilepsy are troubled by photosensitivity. A seizure can be brought on by a flashing light such as a strobe light in a club, and this problem usually arises between the ages of five and nineteen. Although this affects only a small minority, the problem is still there and can be upsetting for the young in particular. It is not just the flashing lights in a disco that can be troublesome, but an ordinary TV screen or computer game, sunlight through the trees or on water, looking out of a window on a train or even looking at a moving escalator. Some people can also find shapes such as checks or stripes troublesome. Photosensitivity can be identified using an electroencephalogram (EEG) which monitors the brain whilst the subject is shown a flashing light.

Febrile seizures can occur in the young, between the ages of six months and six years. These short tonic clonic convulsions may be brought on by a viral infection and result from high body temperatures - the name febrile means to do with a fever. I remember my baby son having one. I thought I had passed on epilepsy, but it turned out to be a single febrile seizure, brought on by a temperature of 103 degrees. This was reduced by bathing him with a cold sponge. A febrile seizure does not require long term treatment, unless complications develop.

Several tonic clonic seizures occurring one after the other with no period of recovery, result in a condition called status epilepticus. This, fortunately rare, event can be particularly dangerous and constitutes a medical emergency. Absence status - absence seizures occurring one after the other - is far less serious, but can still be particularly unpleasant. The patient looks to be in a trance-like state. When this happened to me, I remembered nothing for two days except one bit of one day. I saw a notice above a door which read "Duck". I read the notice but because of the state I was in made no sense of it. Consequently I banged my head rather hard - it hurt! The two days apart from that moment remain a blank. Yes, I think I can say it is unpleasant. Status can also include other types of seizure.

If you witness a seizure, it can appear frightening but the way to handle it is simple: The thing to remember is you cannot prevent the seizure from happening; let it take its course. With a bigger seizure involving a fall, remove harmful objects, don't put anything in the person's mouth and, if possible, put something soft under their head. Once the convulsions stop, simply put the person in the recovery position (if they have saliva around their mouth you could wipe it away) and let them recover in their own time.

Once someone is diagnosed as having epilepsy, they will be put on anti-convulsant treatment. In about eighty per cent of cases this will bring the seizures under control and the person may never be affected again. It is only the other twenty per cent that are not controlled by anti-convulsants. The most effective way of identifying the cause of someone's epilepsy is with an MRI (Magnetic Resonance Imaging) scan. If the area affected by epilepsy can be identified by a scan, it may be possible to help or even cure it by surgery. The scanner is an extremely complex piece of machinery that uses a strong magnetic field, far greater than the earth's own magnetic field, to scan the hydrogen protons in the human body. It has identified the cause of many people's epilepsy. There are no side affects with an MRI scan, unlike an X-ray. However, all earrings, coins, keys etc must be removed from the patient. They then lie down on a flat surface which moves into the machine. Ear plugs are available as the scanner can be quite loud, but the whole thing is completely painless. The scan takes about half an hour and the subject must keep as still as possible . There is also a two way intercom system so contact with the outside world is available throughout the scan.

One of the things I have always found is that my memory is bad. Complaints of poor memory are very common in people with epilepsy, though it does not affect everybody. Possible causes are anti-epileptic drugs, brain damage or frequent epileptic discharges that are not enough to cause a seizure. Of course, not all memory problems are the result of having epilepsy. For many years I have found it difficult to remember things. To give an example, I can watch a film on TV then two weeks later claim that I had never seen it before in my life. Strangely, childhood memories still stick out in my mind very clearly. I find I have to see someone's face several times before recognising them as someone I know. This happened in London on one occasion. I was in the hospital and had a seizure then could not recognise who the doctor was; I spoke to him as if he was a complete stranger. Oddly, I could remember the name, but not put the name to the face.

My children and husband are constantly reminding me to do things. This even includes a simple chore like taking my pills, which should be automatic after a lifetime of doing so, but it isn't. I'm afraid to say I even have to be reminded of things where it is vital to 'stay safe', like standing back from the cooker.

Day to day living can sometimes be quite difficult. For instance, when I go shopping, something will always be forgotten. This means another trip to the shops, crossing dangerous roads. My husband is always saying to me to remind him to tape things off the TV, and what do you think happens? I forget! My sons get quite embarrassed if their friends come to the house and I can't recollect their names. It is sad to think such a large lump of your life is missing for whatever reason, whether it be short term memory loss or even long term memory loss. I find the best way of coping with the problem is to write things down or to say the instruction a few times to myself, preferably out loud.

Learning difficulties may arise from the same cause as epilepsy, but having epilepsy does not mean you will have learning difficulties. Thirty per cent of people with learning difficulties do have epilepsy. Fifty per cent of people with severe learning disability have epilepsy.

The safety of driving is something to be considered. The law varies from country to country. Usually, in the UK, a period of one to two years without a seizure has to be undergone before it is permissible to drive a car.

Do people with epilepsy have a high mortality rate? Overall, someone with epilepsy is statistically more likely to die younger than the population as a whole. More men than women die of something that is epilepsy related, and such a death is statistically more likely for someone under forty years than over. For those in the older age bracket of 75+, death is much more likely to be caused by something unrelated to epilepsy.

Sufferers often wonder whether they are free to carry on their leisure activities without fear or concern. Basically the person should carry on a near-normal lifestyle and enjoy life as far as possible. They should not be over-protected as this can cause psychological problems. With activities, for instance swimming, it is advisable to tell someone who can keep a watchful eye for any difficulties. It is very important to try to lead a normal life as far as possible.

The psychological effects of epilepsy are said to be more distressing than the physical event of a seizure. In my experience, this is quite true.

Years ago a person could be burnt at the stake for being a witch or possessed by evil spirits. In medieval times, epilepsy sufferers were not allowed to partake of the Eucharist in church as the condition was thought to be contagious. In the nineteenth century, people with epilepsy were segregated in the asylum, again because it was believed to be contagious. These ancient misconceptions are still in evidence today. Believe it or not, a survey done by the National Society for Epilepsy in 2000 showed that 4% of people in the UK still believed that epilepsy is caused by the possession of evil spirits.

Part of the Chalfont Centre in the Buckinghamshire countryside, where the National Society for Epilepsy has helped in the care and assessment of people with epilepsy for over 100 years *[Photograph: National Society for Epilepsy]*

From time to time in history, people with epilepsy were even thought to be geniuses. How history turns around. There have been many famous people with epilepsy: Alexander the Great, Joan of Arc, Vincent van Gogh, Julius Caesar, Beethoven, Napoleon, Handel, and more recently Rabbi Lionel Blue and South African cricketer Jonty Rhodes. Many people famous or not, young or old can suffer with epilepsy. As has been shown it is not an uncommon condition.

2   **Childhood years**

O h, my childhood years! There are so many memories, both good and bad. I hardly remember having epilepsy as a little girl. I just remember thinking of it as a daydream. Even my parents seemed to think of the absences as just blank patches in my life. As a child I didn't have many tonic clonic seizures or "the big ones" as they are called by some people.

I do remember a party, though. I couldn't have been more than three or four years old when a big seizure happened at this party. I was in the garden - it's rather blurred a bit vague even - I was carried from the garden to the bedroom upstairs and laid on a bed. My father was called and he carried me home in his arms. I think he realised what the significance of this seizure was. The blank patches had started to make sense. Epilepsy was diagnosed - I had a condition that affects thousands of people and could also affect the rest of my life. At the time, I was unaware of how important this would be. As far I was concerned I had just fallen asleep and I came to wondering what the all the concern was. You see, unless you actually hurt yourself in the course of a seizure there is no pain involved. Indeed, you will not feel pain from injuries sustained during the seizures till after you recover. The whole thing - even though it can look quite dramatic - is the same sensation as going to sleep, and you may feel muddled or confused when it is all over.

Playing safe on three wheels

As a child my condition didn't matter to me. This was not because seizures didn't happen. They did, but typical of any child I just ignored it. My parents, on the other hand, used to worry and were full of archaic ideas about epilepsy, because they were not told any different. They didn't know that six o'clock bed times at the age of eight or nine years old would make no difference, especially in summer. I used to lie in bed on summer nights, with the sunlight streaming through the curtains keeping me awake anyway. I could hear all of the other children playing outside, and there I was in bed. When I became a teenager and went to discos my mother insisted I wear dark glasses because of the flashing lights, I felt so silly. She did not realise that only-five percent of those with epilepsy had photo-sensitivity - their seizures can be brought on by flashing lights. - and that I was not one of them.

My mother used to worry about me on an ordinary bicycle, She thought that with my absences it might be dangerous, which is prob-ably true. Absences only last a few seconds, but whilst riding a bike they could have been fatal. So I had a tricycle from a very early age. I remember well how I used to race my trike up and down the pave-ment, and how I used to love it!

Although I was a tom-boy, I had dolls like any other girl. I used to have 'walky' dolls, 'talky' dolls and fashion dolls. They all used to sit for hours in the 'school room'. The biggest of my dolls was the 'teacher' and she and the other dolls used to have many lessons that I could dream up. My mum was probably happiest then, knowing that I would be safe and could come to no harm in my imaginative little world.

I used to take my pills in a special way. I knew they were not sweets, and I knew I had to take them. By making the procedure fun I made sure I did not miss any medication. My mother used to put them in a dessert spoon at meal times. One was a Phenobarbitone capsule, I can remember the bright orange colour it had. The other was a very tiny round tablet. To an adult these are just two pills, but to a child it opens up a new world - the world of fantasy. I would put the white tablet on top of the capsule. To most people this would make nothing, but with a little imagination it makes a submarine with a lid on it, and this is what it became to my brother and me. The game did not end there. We used to see if we could dive it under the spoon without knocking the lid off - we rarely succeeded, but it was fun any-way, even the creases in the tablecloth were the waves of the sea, and the submarine had to avoid them at all costs.

My love for being a young person meant doing everything every-body else did. That meant tobogganing down the hill in winter, and many times I would fall off and roll in the snow. Like any other child I didn't really care about my own safety.

I was told that many of those with childhood epilepsy grew out of it by the time they reached puberty, and that this would probably hap-

Weathering the Storms - living with epilepsy

pen to me. My seizures were not bad as a child, just absences happening very frequently every day but I remember well looking forward to my twelfth birthday. To me it meant a milestone: the end of an era and the start of a new one. However, for me the new era never really began for instead of the seizures stopping they started to get worse when my periods started. Seizures would come on regularly at period times. Later, when I had my own children this got worse still.

My school years were marvellous, though. My school friends were very kind and supportive. It has always been my experience that young people have far less of a problem with my epilepsy than adults.

I went to a convent school. The teachers were very unsure of me. They were always wary and never quite sure how to handle the situation. I used to get angry at school reports: "Julie does her best under the circumstances"; "Julie tries hard". Comments like that were like a red rag to a bull.

I remember on one occasion, I was so proud when I did a project for geography. The teacher said the one she liked the best would be awarded a prize. I wrote a project on the sea and sailing the many oceans. I always enjoyed writing and spent weeks on this project. It was very thick, almost like a book, and I was so determined to demonstrate that I was as good as anybody else. I was amazed and delighted when the decision had been made. Prize day arrived, the one day of the year when all the teachers, pupils and parents would be present. I would have my moment of glory and would walk up onto the stage with the audience clapping. Then what if . . . . it didn't bear thinking about. Everyone had already thought of it. Suppose I collapsed under the stress, what then? I told everyone not to be silly. The day came, my name was called out, and I slowly walked up the steps to the stage in the big hall, with head held high all of the time, I said to myself: "So what if I do collapse". I accepted the book as my prize and shook hands with the headmistress. There was a roar of people clapping and cheering. My friends clapped especially loud to give me moral support. I walked off the stage with dignity thinking: "Yes, I have done it". That was a day I shall never forget.

By the time I had reached sixteen, the headmistress and the teachers had come to the conclusion that I should not sit my O-level examinations. I never did find out why. Perhaps they thought the stress would bring on seizures, or perhaps they thought that I wouldn't pass them anyway. Of course this made me want even more to sit them. Whether I passed or failed wasn't really the issue here, I felt that I had the right to sit them. The school was very unhappy about this, and made me sit in a separate room from all the other girls. They even asked my mother to be the invigilator for the exams. The school seemed worried I would upset all the other pupils should a seizure take place. I passed some examinations and failed others, but I had shown the school. One of the girls found out I had passed some of them and accused me of cheating because my mother was the invigilator. She spread malicious rumours around the school. I felt that I couldn't win. If I passed I was a cheat, if I failed I was dumb. I was very hurt. My mother was furious and told the girl's parents what she had said, and she was made to apologise to me.

I only passed a few O-levels, but this was despite me having absences throughout the day during lessons. My day would have blank spots throughout. Let me explain. If you were to say the word 'blackout' without the first syllable, it would become 'out'. This is what an absence is like. Just tiny bits of the day gone missing.

I was still able to play tennis, hockey, rounders, netball and even go swimming. I would ask the life guard to watch me whilst I swam, and used only the shallow end of the pool. I must admit that I longed to go up the deep end and dive off the boards, but my mother's strict rule was "no higher than your waist". This also applied when I swam in the sea. For reasons I cannot explain I have never had a seizure of any type in salt or chlorine water. This made me extremely confident when I was swimming. I learnt from a very early age, and by the time I had reached ten or eleven I had passed my Swimming Teachers Association badge which meant from that age onwards I was qualified to teach someone to swim.

I was a very fat child. Nobody knew whether this was because I comfort ate to make me feel better, or whether it was the medication I was taking. Nevertheless, I was quite athletic for my size. Sailing was a great love of mine, and I was a member of the local yacht club from the age of nine.

I rarely ever helmed our sailing boat because of the dangers that could be involved. Instead I acted as a crew member. I would sit on the hull during the stronger winds to stop the boat from turning over. This has to be one of the most exhilarating experiences I have had. There is nothing like going through white-crested waves at a rate of several knots. What a wonderful time my friends and I had. In the summer we used to anchor out at sea and watch the Folkestone's sandy beach fill up with people, and there we were with a picnic and a great expanse of sea around us.

I remember on one occasion my brother took me out sailing and the wind became very strong. The waves were hitting the boat, water was spraying over the hull then suddenly we hit a rock that was hidden by the waves. A large hole appeared near the boat's centre plate, and all my brother could say was: "come on fatty, start getting rid of the water, start bailing out". He carried on being his usual rude and obnoxious self, and I did as I was told. I started to get rid of the water. My brother did not panic. He hung a red ensign upside down at the top of the mast, which he knew would attract attention. Sure enough it was spotted by the crew of the pilot boat, and help came. It was

Despite the risks, I loved messing about in boats

not until twenty years later that I asked myself why did he carry on being so rude, why didn't he panic? Finally, the answer became obvious. I think he wanted the situation to be as normal as possible. Like all brothers, he was always rude to his sister and knew I would accept that, and not worry. Panic is a great stress inducer, stress can increase the chances of having a seizure. He realised this and kept calm, knowing that I would do the same. The chances were I would go without a seizure, and his tactic worked.

Children and young people have always been marvellous towards my condition. Apart from that one instance when I was accused of cheating at school, I was never teased or bullied by other pupils. Young people would watch my every move without it being obvious. When I played in school inter-house matches, my friends would see me have an absence and they would wink at me as a form of moral support, and then smile from one side of their faces to the other.

As a teenager in the late 1960s, I had an afro haircut. I would dress in a kaftan and walk barefoot, constantly spouting "love and peace". My friends at this stage of my life were very aware of my condition, and were very willing to help as best they could. However, when you reach teenage years, a change goes on in your body; not just physically, but mentally too. The way your body appears and the way you think all change in those early years. I began to notice even more how adults were treating me. Was I being treated differently because

I had seizures or was it all part of growing up? I began to think the world owed me a favour, I reached fifteen and got so upset that I tried to take my own life by taking an overdose of the anti-convulsants that were prescribed to reduce seizures. I was found by my mother who rushed me to hospital. Later, I remember opening my eyes and seeing a nurse standing there. She said: "You've had your stomach pumped out. You'll be all right after a sleep, then if you don't mind can you hurry up and vacate the bed, - so we can give it to someone who wants to live". Where was the sympathy I had expected? It finally hit home, and I thought: "I don't want to die, I enjoy living too much." The nurse was in her own way just telling me to get on with my life, and I have done so, despite the few bad moments that we all have. I realised at this point my life would have to be far more laid back and relaxed in style, if I was going to cope. Instead of sailing I took on the role of Race-Officer which meant I would start and finish the races for the yachts from the shore with a klaxon horn- This I enjoyed.

In hindsight, I believe that I had a wonderful childhood with my friends all helping me. As I will explain later, children have a wonderful way of caring and coping, and of trying their best to do what they can to help.

Weathering the Storms - living with epilepsy

3

Is it possible to work?

My working life has been varied. As a child I was never allowed to work on a paper round like all of my friends did. My mother did not like the idea of me using a bicycle in the mornings. She considered a bike to be dangerous, and the mornings have always been my worst time of day for seizures. She also believed that I needed the extra sleep to cope with my epilepsy, so I never had a paper round.

By the age of twelve or thirteen I found work that I enjoyed but did not earn any money for it. The job was writing: I would write a regular article for the local newspaper about that week's sailing at the Yacht Club. One, I remember, described the incident of the hole in the boat that occurred when I was younger. The very long descriptive piece described the colour of the sea that day and how angry it looked compared to usual summer days. I used to hand my article over to the gentleman who wrote for all the yacht clubs in the district. He gave me a helping hand. I no longer felt useless. I wasn't peddling a bike round the district and earning money for it but I enjoyed the writing none the less. I would also describe the yacht races, and note for instance whether it was a close finish or not. I loved it. I was still too young to earn a living so again I wrote. This time it was poetry - and it was published. One of my favourites is a poem called 'To A Sailor - I Understand':

> The waves that wash our shores,
> Vanish into the distant mass of ocean
> Reflecting your thoughts, and your words.
> No-one can understand the silence
> And the solitude that spreads across the sea,
> For this is what you base your life around
> This and the feeling that you're free.
> I understand, Yes I do understand.

It was all very well to have an unpaid job, but by the age of sixteen I had left school and needed to earn my keep. My greatest ambition was to be a nurse. However, I knew this could probably never be because of my condition. At that time my epilepsy was not bad so I snapped up the chance to do what I always wanted to do. I became a nursing auxiliary at a local old people's home. I knew this would be temporary because the epilepsy was steadily getting worse, so I snapped up the opportunity while I had it and enjoyed about a year of nursing. I took blood pressures, temperatures, gave bed baths, and the one thing I shall never forget - the hospital corners on all the beds. The home knew about my condition, but they knew that my absences lasted a split-second, not long enough to cause any harm or put the patient at risk. When the bigger seizures started to become more frequent, I realised that keeping the job was hopeless as I could be putting patients at risk. Despite really loving the job, I knew it would not be fair on either the home or the patients. I remember being very upset by this. The next step was to find another job.

Before giving up work to start a family, I applied for five jobs and I am proud to say that I was successful every time. My idea was not to walk into an interview room and say "I have epilepsy". Instead I said "Good morning my name is Julie, I suffer with epilepsy", and then I described what work I could do.

If you are faced with this problem, let the potential employer know the things you can do rather than the things you can't. Go into the interview room and sell yourself. Never under any circumstances hide from your future employer that you have epilepsy. It is easier to sack you for withholding this fact than for having a seizure in the workplace. If you can think positive thoughts as you go in for your interview this will help enormously. Do not think "if I get the job" but "when I get the job." Always remember an employer and colleagues have the right to know if you have a problem. They are the ones who will help you after all, if you have a seizure. By following this practice, I realised not all people are prejudiced against those with epilepsy, especially in the working world.

I held down two jobs in insurance offices when I left nursing. The first job was filing tiny cards and the other was just sorting through papers. The work was boring and not very enjoyable. I needed to stretch my brain a lot more. What I came to realise was it had nothing whatsoever to do with the fact that I had epilepsy. It was that I was young, and other young people about the same age as me were doing the same menial jobs. I stuck it for about two years then decided enough was enough. A friend of mine could see I had enough of tedious jobs, and that I needed a break. But what could I do at eighteen or nineteen? She said her sister needed a nanny and would I like the job? She knew the problem and was not the slightest bit concerned. "Great", I thought, and there was a bonus - the job was in Madrid. I quickly rushed to get a passport and flew out there. The next eleven months were wonderful. I loved the scenery and the flat we lived in was very luxurious. The child I looked after was about four

years old, and every day I looked after, dressed, played with and fed him. The mother looked on, watching my every move, yet doing nothing to assist. It was wonderful that year, we had a flat over the square in Madrid, and the experience was made even more of a landmark in my life because it was the time when Franco died. People donned black clothes and talked very quietly in the streets, yet a few days later when Juan Carlos was crowned king, there was dancing in the streets. In the flat we didn't go down to the square because the family were concerned for my safety, but we carried on our celebrations in the flat. Before I flew home I treated myself to the most wonderful hand-embroidered shawl as something to remind me of those wonderful few months. The shawl still has pride of place in my wardrobe.

On my return home, I joined another office, this time the job - receptionist and telephonist - was one with a bit of interest in it. This would seem far more stimulating than pushing cards around in an insurance office. During my interview, the employer was very understanding. He smiled and said: "when can you start?" I had never used a switchboard before so I had to be taught. I made a point of explaining to all my colleagues that I could have a seizure at any time. Instead of fear they showed understanding and said they were willing to help should it be necessary. I was in a front office and had to greet all of the visitors. Seizures did happen, some big some small, but I got through the day. Sometimes the telephone would ring and I would answer it, and suddenly I would stop for a few seconds, I wouldn't speak and when I 'returned' I would have to explain the silence on the telephone. Rather than go into a long explanation of what really happened, I would tell a white lie and say it was a bad line and could they please repeat what they had said. It worked every time. When members of the public would come into the office with enquiries, it was slightly harder, I would stop, then sometimes need prompting as to what I was doing or saying. Once again , bluff goes along way and I would just make out that it wasn't my day, No-one ever questioned me or queried my blank spots. It's amazing how you can get through if you try.

It helps to remember that many famous people have suffered with epilepsy, some of them very clever. This was an incentive to me, and made me believe I could hold down a good job. I tried to remember that if they could do it - so could I.

One of the most important things to remember is, there are many, many people who suffer with epilepsy - all over the country. Many have very good well paid jobs. Some are very high profile and are extremely clever men and women. Many people can carry on a normal lifestyle. After all, eighty per cent of epilepsy sufferers are fully controlled by their drugs. Their epilepsy is really of small concern to them, provided they take their medication regularly.

I have come to the conclusion over the years that it is important to know my own limits and stick by that. It is obvious that I am doing too much as seizures will occur. On the other hand it can work the other way. I might not be doing enough to occupy my brain, then I start going into myself and getting depressed. At this point it is important to move and act on it otherwise I find I will be dragged down with the depression. This happened to me a few years back. I remember little about the experience, except that eventually I stopped dwelling on myself , and started to become active. It really didn't matter whether it was paid work or voluntary work. What was important was to do it.

I cannot overstate the need to have a positive attitude and to keep that chin held high at all times. People with epilepsy must realise their worth and try to 'sell' themselves, not the fact that they have the condition. This is very important.

On the other hand, it is interesting to read the results of a poll which was done in 2001, when 2000 epilepsy suffers were asked about employers' reactions towards them: 35% of people polled believed they had lost their job because of epilepsy, and another 38% had experienced prejudice from an employer and 30% of people believed they had failed the initial interview because of epilepsy. One figure that stands out is that 45% of people had experienced prejudice in the workplace. This is particularly high. These are just some of the figures. It is quite appalling to think that nowadays there is still prejudice and misunderstanding. This is why it is very important for the sufferer to really believe in themselves. I have heard about other sufferers who found it hard to get jobs despite getting on very well in the community. Some were unemployed for as many as ten years although constantly trying, despite the fact that these days there are rules and regulations to prevent employers discriminating against disabled people. I sometimes wonder whether the bias is still there. Was I one of the lucky ones, or was it my positive attitude?

4   Relationships: Difficulties and successes

When I was a child I had no trouble forming relationships. The seizures where not bad then and children always accept situations, so I was really just one of the crowd. Life started to get difficult when I reached my teenage years, the hormones started to work and I took an interest in boys. I didn't have that many relationships until I met someone who was mature enough to be able to help when possible yet not be over protective. My first relationship was a holiday romance when I was fourteen. We were on a cruise ship, and my boyfriend was a member of the crew. He was kind and helpful, yet not overbearing. I thought that he was the one for me, but like all holiday romances it came to an end and despite tearful promises that we would write every day to each other, I never heard from him again.

There were other boyfriends, but with most I explained the situation and to them it was a complication. They were no longer interested. I suppose my second big romance was when I was working at a insurance office during the school holidays to gain extra cash. The boy I was working with was about two years older than me and the pair of us just had filing to do. It was boring. An idiot could have done it. Obviously we started talking, only to find we had the same taste in rock bands, we both liked the same foods and neither of us liked cricket. One thing we did take an interest in was snooker. He lived with his parents in a country village not far from my home town of Folkestone, and they had a wonderful snooker room with an enormous table in the middle. His brothers used to visit and we would challenge them to competitions. We would spend hours doing this and I remember enjoying every minute. I told him about my epilepsy as I knew it would be stupid to hide it. I remember him saying "yes, so what?" and from that moment on I started to relax, and enjoy myself. We then told his family and they were very supportive. I would have been about sixteen then. The relationship lasted for over a year. Our big difference was he was not keen on sailing - my one passion, and no amount of asking him to come out with me in the boat ever succeeded. My friends didn't think he was 'macho' enough for them, and he was very much an individual. Time came and went, and off he went to university. I began to feel I would never find the perfect partner, someone who would understand that despite the seizures I was still a normal human being for most of the time.

Impatience is a terrible thing and by the time I reached eighteen, I was determined to find my perfect partner. I met a young good looking man. He seemed perfect at first so I married him. Unfortunately, he loved to drink, and the more seizures I had the more he would drink. He could not cope with the epilepsy. He would get violent and hit me repeatedly, partly due to the fact he liked drink and partly because he was quite scared of my seizures. One seemed to spark the other off. I was three months pregnant and my husband beat the living day lights out of me after I had had many absences. As a result, I lost the baby. Our marriage lasted for just under a year before I knew I would have to file for divorce.

As the old saying goes, "once bitten, twice shy". I was scared of getting into another relationship and having the same problem all over again. Two years passed, I was now about twenty. Where was the happiness that everyone else seemed to have? Then I met the man who was to become my second husband. I was honest from the start with him as I wasn't going to be hurt again. "Fine, OK, what do I have to do?" he said, as if it were as simple to handle as the common cold. I could feel a smile beaming from one side of my face to the other. That was twenty-four years ago. We have been together ever since. He never complains and nor do my two children. They take it as part of life - which it is. Our courting days were wonderful visits to 'ye olde worlde' pubs, playing bar billiards, going to museums and bars and generally touring wherever we felt like it. Even now, I can honestly say our relationship is as good. There are days when I feel sorry for myself, but my husband is like a tonic and tells me not to be so silly. When the days are bad, he is perfect. No-one could ask for more.

There are other relationships besides those with boys. Some members of my close family have never, and will never, be able to accept the fact that I have epilepsy. To be honest they don't want to know. They never enquire about my health, and get upset when I tell them the details of various seizures. Despite these family members, there are many friends, acquaintances and colleagues who are always willing to help and listen while I talk. I have a counsellor who knows me well, and I talk to her about anything and everything. It is very important for a person with a disability to be able to confide in someone, to explain fears, sad moments and painful moments. Family members are sometimes too close to discuss the situation. After all they see seizures every day. They don't enjoy it, they cope with it in their own way, and are there when needed.

I believe one thing is obvious: that is it takes an extremely special person to cope with a disability. To partner someone who is disabled takes a lot of love and dedication. There must be give and take on both sides. Epilepsy is not like being in a wheelchair or having a stick. It is a condition that cannot be seen unless it occurs, so most of the time the sufferer is fine. However, it can be difficult for a partner as they have to be ready to react at a moment's notice, at any time and in any place, in order to manage the situation.

My relationship with my children - my boys who are now eighteen and twenty - is excellent, I have always found honesty to be the best policy. From a very early age they have had to find a way to cope with my seizures. They handle it like their father does, as part of everyday life.

Socialising is another form of relationship, a relationship with people in general. There are ways of socialising with people without having too much to drink. There are hobbies to pursue and places to see, and things to do, without epilepsy getting in the way. Given the right attitude, it need not be a noose round the sufferer's neck.

5   Marriage, pregnancy and motherhood

Everyone was concerned about me on the day I got married to my second husband. Unlike my first wedding, this was to be in front of all of our friends. It would firstly be at the Register Office for the civil ceremony, then on to the church for the blessing.

Where epilepsy is concerned, nothing is sure, especially in a high pressure situation. Everyone was wondering whether I would collapse. We took our vows in front of the Registrar, who had been briefed in advance. There were no problems - so far, so good! Now for the church. I remember having small black-outs as I walked up the aisle on the arm of my uncle. I was nervous, but probably no more so than any other bride, but in my case I had the added pressure of frequent absences. Fortunately, nothing more serious occurred. I felt proud as I walked back on the arm of my new husband and when we posed for the photographs outside the church.

Next we went on to the reception. Again absences were coming on during the time we where there. The secret was not to fight or ignore them, but to take them as part of life. It was not my epilepsy that let me down on the day but something else. I went to the toilet at the reception then tucked my wedding dress into my knickers, and emerged showing my legs! This just goes to prove I make the same mistakes as any body else.

A few years on we started to think about a family. One of my family members said I should adopt. Whether this is because they thought the children would not be 'right in the head', or whether they thought I wouldn't be capable of giving birth they didn't say. I remember telling this to the doctor at the National Hospital for Neurology in London. He just grinned when I asked if it could be possible. The reply came: "of course, Julie. There's only a small chance that your child would inherit epilepsy." I was so delighted, it was like a massive explosion going off inside me.

During pregnancy my anti-convulsants were lowered so the baby wouldn't be harmed by them. As the anti-convulsants had been lowered more seizures started occurring so I had to be careful not to put myself at risk and so that no harm would come to my baby.

With the lower dose of medication, seizures were happening more frequently, many every day. For my own safety, I needed to be watched a lot of the time. When my husband was at work, neighbours, friends and local children would pop in for half an hour or so, just to check that all was well. My kitchen became a bit like a cafeteria, but all this was being done for me.

The local children were marvellous. There were about nine or ten of them. It started one day with a little girl standing on the doorstep. She said: "my mum says you have 'eperpepsy' and you fall down sometimes. She said you might need help - can I help?" The child was no older than nine and her name was Helen. I was concerned that my epilepsy might be a problem for her, but she looked at me with big wide eyes so I hadn't the heart to say "no". I asked her in and she made me a cup of coffee as she realised I had to be careful with the kettle. So here was I, just a few months pregnant and with a nine year old to look after me. She obviously liked it because she brought her friends with her until eventually there were about nine or ten of them. They would be in the house when I wanted to bath, I would leave the door ajar and they would listen out for sounds of a fit, and then they would be on the ball and would charge up the stairs to protect me.

Local youngsters proved very helpful when my children were young

I had a seizure on one of Helen's visits when she was with her friend. I fell on to the living room floor and remember when I recovered consciousness there were the two children sobbing. They had finally seen what everyone seems to dread. I whispered "I'm sorry." They looked at each other then at me. Helen said: "you haven't upset us, Julie. We're just sorry you have to go through this every single time." I was sore with carpet burns, but suddenly it didn't seem to matter and I smiled back at them.

The youngsters were great. They would walk to the local shops, one on either side of me. I wanted to thank them for all these things they did for me. The only thing I could think of was to bake them party cakes on their birthdays. I created all sorts of cakes from crinoline ladies to a newspaper with funny headlines. I had the ability to ice cakes and enjoyed it, and it was my way to say how my I appreciated the help.

I had to think of a way to get up and down stairs without putting my baby at risk by falling. My husband thought of a way to do this. I would walk upstairs sideways and then slide down the stairs step-by-step on my bottom. Because the kitchen had a concrete floor, I would try to stay out of it unless someone else was in the house or when it was absolutely necessary. Cooking was done only when someone else was in the house, never by myself.

As the months passed I grew bigger and bigger because one of the tablets I was taking was increasing my weight. I went to hospital on regular occasions for blood pressure tests, and to check my weight. On one occasion I had to be weighed and the scales did not go up far enough so they had to bring some different scales. They said it was a meat-scale from the kitchen! The embarrassment was overwhelming. The only thing left to do was to smile and laugh with everybody else. I thought: "Blow these tablets!". They control the seizures a little but I felt like a barrage balloon.

I couldn't wait for the birth of my first baby, I wanted to see a perfect boy or girl lying in my arms. A week or two before the due date I was taken into hospital with high blood pressure. Eventually the day came and I was put on gas and air. The screaming and the bad language I used was second to none - those poor nurses. Everyone was waiting and watching, hoping I would not have a fit. The absences occurred and I could feel the perspiration falling off my brow. I remember saying to myself: "come on Julie you can do it, he or she is going to be perfect." Then an eight pound, twelve ounce baby boy came into the world. I cried with joy. I had done it without a major seizure.

The baby spent his first few days shaking with withdrawal symptoms from the medication he had shared with me for the last nine months, but this soon abated. However, it was important to test my child to see whether he had epilepsy. This was done at the age of six months and fortunately we were told that our son had no trace of epilepsy. I was overjoyed. The chances were slight, but I must admit I was worried.

I wrote a poem as a celebration of my son's life, it was my way of saying thank you.

Poem for Paul

What thought lies behind those big blue eyes?
Are you a demon, a saint, or just a baby in disguise?
Your world is full of wonder and delight,
To you the simple things of life are a wonderful sight.
Everything is so new,
There is so much to do.
Look at colours and touch everything around,
Pull the dogs tail - hear it make that crying sound.
Toys to cuddle, toys that make a noise
Dolls for the girls, helicopters for the boys.
The tears the crying which mean so much,
The loving feel of a mothers touch -
All this is important in the early years
The laughter, the dreams, the hope - and the fears.

The birth was a wonderful happening, but now the hard work was beginning. Marriage had to be team-work with both of us helping the other. My husband's paid job was only part of his day. He had to come home and help me with our child as he knew I had to have some rest, otherwise seizures could have occurred. I never did the night feed. My husband did those. He had a broken sleep pattern then a busy day at work ahead of him. Life was definitely hard for both of us - but it was rewarding.

In the morning my work would start. I would never carry Paul around the house or up the stairs. My husband would bring him downstairs in the morning. If I wanted to move the baby from room to room, I would push him around the house in a buggy. Feeding, too, was done in a buggy. I would kneel down next to the buggy, lean well backwards with my arm outstretched with the bottle in my hand, then if I did have a fall I would probably fall backwards and not on top of my baby. Nappy changing was done with Paul on a mat and me

Weathering the Storms - living with epilepsy

kneeling to one side, rather than kneeling between his legs. Again this was to avoid falling on top of him.

Bathing was the most fun. I couldn't bath Paul on my own - it was far too risky, so local children would come and assist. In particular this would involve Helen, but sometimes there would be as many as half a dozen helpers on bath days . It was often impossible for me to get near the baby bath because of all the children! From the back I would watch the young people doing the work. It was a jolly time. Even the baby was giggling the whole time. There were other times though, when the baby's crying never seemed to stop. It would just go on and on. Teething was a particularly bad time,

Two years later, I had another son, David. he was quite a handful when he was young and was diagnosed as being hyperactive. When he was very young, we would push his buggy backwards and for- wards for hours over a slight bump between two rooms, trying to rock him to sleep or just to calm him down.

Special precautions were still necessary when I was alone with the boys. Neither of them were allowed to crawl around the house as I could have fallen on top of one of them. As they got older it became less difficult, but we would put them in a play pen for their own safe- ty in the early years with all their favourite toys.

Like all youngsters, the boys had birthday parties and I was deter- mined that these should be enjoyable. In fact, they became famous events. Not only did I invite their friends, all the local young people, my friends and relatives, but I managed to organise it without falling over. Everyone had a great time. There were party hats, crackers, home made cakes like I have described, enough food to feed an entire army and prizes for the games we played. I was determined my children should lack nothing. It got to the point where my children were asked to all the local parties.

They also had their friends around for tea and to play. I made friends with their friends' mothers, and the mothers would come and visit, too. The whole thing would be turned into a social occasion and we shared the responsibility for looking after the smaller children.

Everyday chores still had to be done, though.. Because it was such a strain looking after two small children, outside help was called in to lend a hand with the housework. The home-help was lovely and very kind. She understood the problems I had, and realised that I wanted to do some of the housework myself. That way I could hold my head high and say I was as good as anybody else, something that is quite important to someone with a disability.

My seizures were probably at their most violent and most frequent at this stage of my life. The extra work and the need to prove myself added up to extra stress. I was still very large and I was still having seizures. Eventually, the doctors decided to take me off my tablets and try another medication.

The early years were difficult times. The boys started school and although it was not very far away, the journey meant crossing roads which was something I would try to avoid at all costs. So someone else took the boys to school. I missed taking part in this aspect of their school lives. When they got older they were big enough to walk to school. I would wave them off to school each morning and many times I would close the door and feel the tears rolling down my cheek. This was part of their lives that I didn't enter into.

I made a point of enjoying all the times we did have, such as Guy Fawkes night. I would have to hold sparklers at a distance and stand well back from the bonfire. One year my children and their friends made a really good Guy to go on top of the bonfire, so I made them a special cake shaped like a bonfire.

From a very early age my sons have had to learn to look after themselves and cater for mum when a seizure would occur. Throughout their lives they have had to know what first aid to give. They were taught to accept the situation and carry on regardless. I have always tried to make sure my children lacked nothing and at the same time were never ashamed of their mum. They are now young men, confident and full of energy.

Weathering the Storms - living with epilepsy

6   Miscellaneous seizures

There are many seizure types. For instance, there are some that last for little more than the flicker of an eye, and these are called absences. During an absence, for a mere moment in time nothing seems to make sense. Does this make the seizure any less dangerous than a full blown tonic-clonic, falling down, seizure? Although they are hardly noticeable and for just a second there is blackness, I have learnt from my own experience that absences can have a nasty way with them. For instance, on two or three occasions I have walked into a moving car in the town. On one occasion a car got so close that when I came out of the absence I could feel the warm rubber brushing against my legs. I realised then that although absences are not very noticeable to the onlooker, to the sufferer they can be just as dangerous as a major frothing-at-the-mouth fit.

The 'big', or tonic clonic, seizures are the ones everyone knows. For some people it entails a dramatic scream, a fall, then shaking profusely on the floor. These seizures are the ones renowned for causing damage to the sufferer.

I have had many serious falls, some actually involving plastic surgery. On one occasion I fell through a plate glass door. The only people in the house were six year old Paul and four year old David. Paul told David to stay and comfort me whilst he ran to a neighbour for help. Both boys were crying, but neither showed signs of panic. The neighbour called an ambulance and I ended up in the local casualty ward. There were shards of glass stuck in my head, and I remember the nurse saying each time she removed another piece "just one more dear", but still she kept finding more to pluck out. This was over fifteen years ago but I still have a worried feeling about glass, and have a 'thing' about going near it. I don't think those terrifying moments will ever fade.

On another occasion I fell on top of a television table. The corner of the table caught my chin, entered my cheek and came out near my top lip. It was a horrible sight to see. I was on my own in the house, I just got up to change channel on the television, and that is the last thing I can remember. My husband and my son found me, and sent my son to phone for an ambulance. That was another fall I shall never forget. The scar is still there on my face , but thanks to the wonders of plastic surgery it is much less noticeable than it could be. My face looked a sight for many weeks as the bruising and swelling engulfed about half of my face. We had to buy a new piece of carpet to cover the blood stains. Several years later we bought a new carpet and I was glad to see the back of that memory. This is probably the most painful seizure-related injury I have had.

What sufferers have to bear in mind is that, although they do the physical suffering, the stress and strain on close family and friends is also quite great. Especially with a fall such as I have described, they go through the upset too.

Other serious injuries can happen during everyday chores. For instance, on one occasion I fell head-first into a bath of boiling water. I had, rather stupidly, only run the hot tap. My husband pulled me out and poured jugs of cold water over me to ease the burning, before calling for an ambulance. I was covered in blisters and still have some of the scars today.

Fairly recently I had a seizure at the National Hospital in London. I was in the doctor's consulting room and apparently sent his papers flying all over the desk and onto the floor before being taken to a side room to rest. I remember little or nothing about the event. When I started to get back into the real world, I felt embarrassed and small but I tried to keep smiling. We left the hospital. My husband was holding onto me as we crammed ourselves into a packed tube train. At Kings Cross station another smaller seizure took place. This sometimes happens. They come in clusters or groups. I have noticed that after I have had a seizure, absences come on very frequently for the rest of the day.

On many occasions I have fallen down stairs. My family insist on walking behind me when I go upstairs and in front of me when we go down, so that they can catch me if necessary. They are always reminding me to hold onto the banister when I come down the stairs.

A smoothing iron is also a dangerous implement. I have wrapped the cord of an iron around myself and again I burnt myself badly. Now I do not iron unless there is somebody else in the house. My family help me a lot by doing their own ironing, so I only need to do it occasionally.

These are some of the sensational seizures which for most people may occur only once or twice in a lifetime. However, no seizure should be taken lightly and all types may cause injury. On many occasions I have collapsed in the street and have been taken to hospital with all sorts of cuts and bruises.

Weathering the Storms - living with epilepsy

Some of the smaller injuries can be quite painful . I have broken my nose on more than one occasion. This can be extremely painful. My ribs have been cracked or broken many times and it takes only a little movement round the rib for this to be very painful.

Some epilepsy sufferers end up with minor injuries almost on a daily basis. A carpet burn, caused by friction between the carpet and the shaking person, can hurt as much as other types of burn. And of course bruising occurs virtually every time a large seizure happens. This is because it usually involves a fall, a bang on a door or maybe bumping a piece of furniture. These are typical for me.

Absences can be troublesome. A blackout can occur whilst crossing the road. Or it may involve missing a stair. And there's grasping a cup of hot coffee and wrapping your hands around the cup, resulting in a burn. Often I don't see things on the floor so I trip over them. These are not lethal, but all are potentially dangerous.

Seizures can be strange. Just the other day I felt a larger seizure coming on, and that was the last thing I remember. During the seizure I removed all of the covers from the cushions in our living room. Strangely enough, the last thing I had said to myself before retiring to bed the night before was that I would wash the cushion covers the next day. I felt the seizure coming on, sat down and then feathers were everywhere, flying all over the living room. Yet I don't remember doing it, I just saw the mess I had made!

My worst time of day is the morning. More seizures happen in the morning than any other time of day. I don't know why. I can never remember getting out of bed, getting dressed or washed, or even walking down stairs. It may be because I am having small seizures of one type or another. Because of this confused state, I can put my clothes on inside out, my shoes on the wrong feet, and make coffee with cold water. Sometimes my family will come down the stairs and try to hold a conversation with me, I either grunt a reply of some sorts or stare at the music channel on the television. If someone says: "put that cup down", strangely enough I do it. To me the morning is nothing but a period of blankness, I can't see or hear anything. Nothing really seems to fall into place for sometimes up to a couple of hours afterwards, sometimes it can be as little as a few tens of minutes. My husband is sometimes able to get me out of my confusion by talking to me. What causes this state? It is the result of continuous 'small' seizures. My family accept it as an everyday part of life.

It is so strange how my seizures have altered over the years. In my childhood the absences were a major part of the day. During the teenage years the larger seizures slowly started to appear and became an every day occurrence about the time of my marriage. In recent years the attacks have been suppressed to the extent that I no longer scream during a grand mal, I just mumble. Instead of violently shaking I simply shudder. The down side of this appears to be the bad mornings described above. These changes are really quite amazing.

Fortunately, my case is not typical. Epilepsy is controlled for eighty per cent of sufferers. This means that with regular medication there is not a problem and seizures happen just occasionally. What is important in all cases with any disability is to think positively and to take each day as it comes. Nothing is certain with epilepsy, one day may be a bad one but the next may be good. Life can be enjoyed despite a disability so long as this is realised. If you pick yourself up every time it happens, you will be half-way to dealing with the condition.

7 Attitudes and opinions

In the Middle Ages, people with epilepsy might well have been con-demned for witchcraft because their seizures were thought to be the result of possession by evil spirits. In the nineteenth century an epileptic seizure would often lead to the sufferer being confined in a lunatic asylum. What is more, they would have been segregated because epilepsy was thought at the time to be contagious. This was all a long time ago and things have improved a great deal since then. Fortunately, this improvement is ongoing and I have seen several changes for the better during my forty five years.

As I mentioned earlier, sitting examinations was not easy and entailed many problems. The attitudes of the teachers, and of the pupil who accused me of cheating, were strange to say the least.

I had needlework classes at school which should have been enjoy-able, but were not. We used electric sewing machines. On one occa-sion I had a absence and nearly sewed my fingers under the needle. It frightened me so badly that I didn't want to use a sewing machine again. My mother spoke to the teachers about it, and it was agreed that I should sew by hand. However, instead of trying to encourage me or help me to enjoy sewing, I think they cast me off as a failure. I would sit at the back of the class every week and sew by hand. If the seams where not straight, or were even slightly out, I was made to unpick them and start again. The teacher had no sympathy and gave me no encouragement to succeed. It took me three years to make a skirt, by which time, needless to say, it did not fit me.

The school - a convent - had a mixture of day pupils and boarders. I remember having to live at school during a period when my mother had to go into hospital. None of the neighbours offered to have me. Perhaps it was not convenient for them. Or was it because I would be a bit of a handful with absences to think about and medication to be taken three times a day? I will never know, and perhaps I am reading too much into it. Whilst staying at the school, the teachers gave me a room to myself - just in case I upset the rest of the girls who were all in a dormitory. It got very lonely at night. I could hear the muffled sounds of the girls talking in the next room, and I just curled up in a ball, extremely lonely, wondering why I couldn't be with them.

Some ten years ago I was challenged by an old couple for having an orange 'disability' badge displayed in the car. They couldn't believe I was disabled. They said to me: "disabled, you don't look disabled, look at you." Instead of ignoring the remark, which I should have done, I started making excuses for myself. I said I had epilepsy, and their reply was: "Huh! This spot is for people like us, people with real disabilities." I was very angry and I admit that if they had been forty years younger I probably would have hit them - but I respected their age. Instead I turned my back on all their foul comments and slowly walked away making sure my head was held high. Although attitudes have changed over the years, there are still some who will believe archaic, strange ideas and will never be convinced otherwise.

I collapsed whilst on a trip out a few years ago, and was convulsing on the pavement. A man walking his dog let the animal step all over me. More than once, I have been unconscious, recovering from a seizure and have been mistaken for a drunk.

It is not just strangers who can act differently, but neighbours as well. On one occasion I collapsed in our house and had a nasty fall at about ten o'clock one night. An ambulance arrived with its sirens and lights going and a neighbour came out and grumbled about the noise. As I was being taken from the house on a stretcher semi-conscious this was all they could find to say.

Epilepsy affects different people in different ways. Those are some of the bad memories I can think of. On the other hand there are many good attitudes towards epilepsy. Just recently, in 2001 I had a slight seizure at King's Cross underground station. My husband caught me, and he said that about fifteen people stopped to see if they could help.

Young people tend to be the ones without fear, probably because they have been taught what epilepsy is. Myths and legends seem to stay with the older generation, though this is not always the case.

There will always be the ignorant few. Considering this is now 2003, the amount of fear I have come across is minimal. A friend explained that she had no fear of epilepsy and knew in advance what to do should a seizure take place. She is one of the few to remain calm and not panic. On the other hand, a disabilities professional said that until she met me she was frightened, particularly of the unexpected. She said: "If you don't understand you become afraid, not necessarily for yourself but for the sufferer."

Having spoken to just two people, I decided to speak to others to see if I could find out the general public's feeling towards epilepsy. In my home town of Welwyn Garden City, I asked twenty-five people in shops, in the streets and parks to see what their views were.

The information I came back with was quite revealing. Most people said they were afraid of epilepsy. Later, I wondered whether this was because of the condition, or simply because they didn't know what to do to help. If someone had a heart attack in front of them, it would be reasonable to panic and be afraid because they wouldn't know what to do for the best.

There were people I tried to question who wanted nothing to do with me. When I explained I had epilepsy, some were positively rude. Most of these seemed to be those over the age of sixty. They would look me up and down when I told them I had epilepsy. When I told them it was not controlled properly they did not seem happy at all, and couldn't wait to get away. Most seemed to be very wary and unsure, but this was less so with younger people.

I spoke to people right across the age spectrum so as to get a reasonable idea of their views. There was only one man who knew what to do should a seizure take place, and he was aged forty five. Older people seemed to think the sufferer would be embarrassed, and they would be embarrassed for the sufferer. Yet if someone broke their leg would they feel embarrassed then?

It was reassuring to find that no-one believed in epilepsy being related to demonic possession, despite a national survey indicating that 4% of the UK population still do (see The Fact and Figures First). In fact some actually laughed at this idea.

Many of those below the age of forty five said they did not know the best thing to do, but they believed they would try to use their common sense. For instance, one person said that if the sufferer was clutching a knife or convulsing near a chair, these harmful objects should be removed. My impromptu survey covered many ages, and always those in the group from twelve to forty-five excelled with common sense.

I also surveyed the pupils at one of the schools I visited during a lecture tour. Most of them said that they were worried when they first saw me have an absence. They added that this was mainly out of concern because they didn't know what to do. It was not fear of the seizure, but ignorance. Once it had been explained to them what to do, they were all confident of being able to handle any seizure without much worry. If people don't understand epilepsy, it can be frightening. Of course, this does not just apply to epilepsy. It is only natural to become afraid of any situation that you don't understand.

I was pleased to find that a large majority of the young people surveyed knew what to do. They were not sure where epilepsy came from. Some thought it might have been passed down from generation to generation - in fact this is rare. None believed in demonic possession. Young people's attitudes are pleasing to see. They seem to have no difficulty in accepting someone with epilepsy into their community. For instance they could find no reason not to be friends with such a person. The contrary was in fact true. They would actually want to help and they would feel sorry for the sufferer because seizures might take up some of their days. To miss pieces out of your day, especially when you are young is unthinkable!

The attitude of the sufferer is very important. He or she needs to have a very positive attitude and be able to exude an air of confidence. To be negative about yourself, and to have an "I can't" attitude, will reflect on the way other people will treat you. In general people like to see a positive attitude coming from the person. This is not just with epilepsy but with any disability. A good attitude makes people feel comfortable and more relaxed. They feel they can handle the situation better, and therefore are more able to help the sufferer.

In this book there is no such concept as: "I can't". If you look hard enough, there is always a way to do something, it may mean that you have to think about it quite a lot, but don't worry it will come right in the end. It is very important for the attitude of the sufferer to be a good one, just as much as the attitude of the people around them to be helpful, caring and positive.

It is all very easy to say "I won't do that because I might get hurt", or "What if I have a seizure when I'm cooking, walking outside or even looking after my family?" I have come to the conclusion you cannot say this. Anyone may get knocked down by a car tomorrow after all. Having a condition such as epilepsy takes courage and a particular state of mind. Any person with any disability must try to fill themselves with confidence and self-esteem, but this is very difficult. I used to think I lost my dignity when I had a fall. Even now in middle age I sometimes still think it. To maintain confidence and self-esteem is something that has to be worked at, sometimes over several years. The real secret is to believe in yourself, and not regard yourself as a second rate citizen. This is the correct, though not always easy, attitude to have.

My own positive attitude has paid off in the past. I thought I could hold down a job in a local charity shop as a voluntary helper. The attitude of the staff towards me was one of fear and shrugging shoulders, and "well I don't really think . . ." I tried to explain to them if they were not happy with my work after a couple of months I would go without argument, but that they should give me a chance. They took me on. I remember those early days. They really were very worried about me being there. I was put in the back room away from the general public, sorting clothes and hanging them up, nothing very strenuous. The two months passed, and they were willing to keep me on. They had finally accepted the fact that from time to time I would have an absence or a more serious seizure, but I didn't worry about it, so why should they?

In the end they were wishing me to do well. They took an interest in my condition, and even put a poster up so that the staff could see from the poster the first aid steps to take. There were occasions when the larger seizures would happen, but the ladies, most of them over the age of sixty, took it as a common occurrence and did not worry about it at all.

Now, instead of a backroom job I work on the counter, dealing with the public. Seizures, particularly absences occur, but neither the customers nor the staff seem to worry. Why is this? Because I don't worry! The ladies in the shop explain to the customer what is happening but now do so without fear in their voices. They have finally developed confidence in me. Sometimes, I regain full consciousness within seconds, but at other times I take longer. Now though, everyone in the shop takes the condition as part of me, and deals with it accordingly. On the really bad days, I have to telephone to say that I can't travel to the shop because of too many seizures. The staff reply in such a caring, matter of fact way and ask if I need any help. These were the ladies who at one time were fearful and wary of me, but have now become carers as well as colleagues.

I have explained about other people's ideas. However, there is something more important than that. What do I think? Am I ashamed of my seizures? To say I am not would be totally untrue. I have always had that part of me which wants to hide them away. Yet I have had them so long that they are a normal part of my life. All these years on I mumble the words "have I had a seizure?", when I actually know I have. I wait for my family's bright reply. A reassuring reply that shows they are not ashamed, so why should I be? I think maybe if the condition wasn't so spontaneous I would be able to treat it more lightly. One of these days I will lose these thoughts and feelings, and will be able to say that I am not ashamed. I have come to the conclusion that your world is as big or small as you want it to be, you are the controller.

8   Before and after a seizure

E very epilepsy sufferer is different where seizures are concerned. Some have warnings or premonitions of a seizure, and some don't, and there are different types of warning. Everyone has a different way of coping with the aftermath, some taking longer to get over a seizure than others. Epilepsy is very much an individual condition. So how does it affect me?

My speech cuts out in an absence and there is a short period of 'nothingness'. When I return to normality my eyesight returns, there is no longer the blackness. Sometimes I suffer from slight confusion and a feeling of not knowing anything, or just being lost for a few seconds. On other occasions I can get by almost without realising that a seizure has occurred, perhaps experiencing only the slight flutter of an eyelid and blurred vision. These are smaller seizures.

The warning I get of a larger seizure (for instance, a tonic clonic or complex partial), is best described by trying to imagine your head slowly filling up, like a bucket of water gradually getting fuller and fuller. Eventually you reach the point when the water can get no deeper, then you fade into a blackness. For some larger seizures I don't get any warning at all, and simply drop to the floor without warning.

Coming to after a seizure is completely different again, and everyone's experience is unique. Typical for me is to find myself lying on the floor wanting to open my eyes. It is quite hard work getting them to open fully as they do not want to co-operate to begin with. Eventually I manage it, and I then try to move my arms and legs in order to lift them off the ground. I find that they can hardly move, and a lot of physical strength is required. So I lie there for quite a while. I need help to get up. My muscles are still flexing and feel very tender. Sometimes I finish convulsing then lie on the floor, either fast asleep or semi-conscious.

After a seizure I get a most revolting taste in my mouth. I always try to find something sweet to drown the taste, perhaps lemonade or a sticky bun. My appetite decreases and my sense of taste is impaired. Despite wanting sweet food, I can only eat very little. My family have realised over the years that this is the case, so when they prepare food for me, I am only given enough to feed a bird and no more! My appetite usually returns by the next day, and the strange taste effect goes after a few hours.

It is usually not possible to get back to a normal life straight after a large seizure. The recovery time varies from person to person and depends upon the type of seizure and the depth of it. In my case, full consciousness does not return for several hours. For most people a sleep or rest is a big help.

I have delivered many lectures on epilepsy and find that the smaller seizures - absences - prove to be a nuisance because of the frequent blank spots and confusion. However, after being prompted I can always get back to what I was saying. I forewarn the audience that I may black out briefly, and they quickly get used to it.

Whilst giving a lecture, I have occasionally collapsed. However, on returning to normality I have been able to finish speaking, sitting down. Under these circumstances, the lecture is not very good because it sounds like a piece of machinery grinding on and on, rather than being spoken with any feeling.

I had a seizure in a van whilst on my way to give a talk to the National Society for Epilepsy. That familiar sensation came on, and the blackness then nothing. I was unconscious for about fifteen minutes. I remember trying to open my eyes and lift my tilted head. I knew I had to deliver a talk within three quarters of an hour, but my head was swirling. Nothing stayed in focus and voices sounded very distorted even muffled. We drove on to the hospital. The driver tried to bring me round by talking to me about why I was in the vehicle, and above all what I was just about to do. I had no recollection at all. I barely knew my own name. My speech sounded slurred and there was even a slight stammer. My hands and legs were shaking. When it finally sank in that I was about to deliver a lecture, fear flushed through my body. We arrived and explained what had happened during the journey. I was given the option of not speaking. However, even though I felt rough, my sheer pigheadedness would not let me give in. I spoke. It wasn't brilliant but the important thing to me was that I did it. Furthermore, the audience were appreciative that I had made the effort and applauded loudly.

I mentioned my pigheadedness. After I have a large seizure my personality seems to change. People ask after me, trying to help but I snap at them or even shout. This can go on for an hour. I become very head-strong and determined. At the same time, my confusion is great and sometimes I don't recognise people. I will swear that I have never seen them. On one occasion I looked at myself in a mirror and started arguing with myself as I had no idea that the person in the glass was me. My family have never forgotten this incident.

For all this confusion, something strange shines through. After one seizure I could not remember who I was or where I was. But something strange sprang into my mind - a number. I guessed it was a telephone number. I dialled the number as I needed help. I had no idea who I was dialling but I did it anyway. A man's voice spoke so quietly that I did not recognise it at first. I spoke and the voice recognised me instantly. It went on to reassure me, reminding me of where I was and who I was. Whose number was it? It was my husband's. Somehow I had remembered his work number. Instantly, help was on hand to quieten me down. He spoke firmly. He wanted me to be safe. Once he had done all this I felt a lot more comfortable. I have to thank my memory because it didn't forsake me when I most needed it.

One thing remains the same during every recovery process. What is it? The need to apologise every time I have a seizure, particularly to strangers. I think this dates back to when some members of my family would get embarrassed when seizures occurred. You would think that some forty years on from my first epileptic seizure it is something that I would drop. I can't, not yet, but maybe I will one day soon.

What an epilepsy sufferer needs is hope. Hope that one day their condition will be controlled, or indeed just stop spontaneously. They always have to believe that it will happen sooner or later, next week or years from now. Having this attitude makes it much easier to bounce back after a seizure, and to cope with epilepsy.

9 A day in the life

Depending on how bad someone's epilepsy is, it will have some effect on their day to day life. For most people, once the epilepsy is controlled by medication, there is usually no problem and normal life can be resumed. For the twenty per cent of sufferers who are not properly controlled, such as myself, the day has to be thought about and planned most carefully to cope with the frequent seizures.

Being particularly prone to seizures first thing in the morning, I keep safe by getting dressed whilst sitting on the bed. I go to the bathroom leaving the door ajar so that family members can hear if I fall. Going downstairs I take one step at a time, holding onto the banister. On reaching the living room, the first thing I do is to remove junk that has been left on the floor by my sons, and to tidy up the furniture. It is important to have a clear space.

The kitchen is the next stop for a nice cup of coffee. I make sure I stand well back from the kettle just in case I have an absence and scald myself. I try to move out of the kitchen as soon as I can because it has a concrete floor which would make (and has made) a painful landing. Even sitting down to drink a cup of coffee has to be thought about. Sometimes, during a small seizure I try to carry on what I was doing before the attack took place. On one occasion I was making a cup of coffee and carried on making it. However, it was with last night's cold water. I even drank it! I came to and thought that my coffee tasted revolting.

I sit well back on my chair, as sitting on the edge would turn a seizure into a fall. I try to put the cup down in between sips and never cradle it in my hands. That, too, could be dangerous. It is not always easy to remember these things, and my family are constantly reminding me of the need to stay safe.

The rest of my day comprises my voluntary work, my lectures and looking after the house. The housework isn't too bad to do. I have some help in the form of a cleaner for a couple of hours each week, but I make a point of doing some of the work myself. My pride makes me do it. I don't do the ironing though. Many years ago, I dropped a hot iron on myself and was badly burnt. Dusting means using a long-handled feather duster for the high places to avoid having to stand on a chair. When washing up I always try to remember to run the hot and cold taps together to reduce the risk of getting scalded.

It is fairly easy for me to do the chores provided I don't rush them. For many years, everybody in the family helped. My two sons and my husband were brilliant. If they thought I looked a little vacant or sleepy they would take over and would do the washing up, cleaning, dusting or washing. I find that it is best not to push myself and try to achieve too much. These days, the boys are older and cannot be expected to be on hand all the time so the housework is done with help from my cleaner, we do it together.

Twice a week I do my voluntary work at a charity shop in the town, just over a mile away. I could go by bus, but I came to the conclusion many years ago that using a bus was a bad step. If I make the slightest shake or flicker of an eye, people tend to panic and I have found it can cause chaos on the bus. So I use taxis. It works out quite a bit more expensive, but for the peace of mind it gives me I find it worthwhile. I am well known to the local taxi drivers who cope well if I have a seizure whilst in their cab.

In the town I walk on the inner side of the pavements, well away from the traffic. When I have to cross roads I am continually looking out for vehicles in order to give myself maximum protection. Sometimes I have a friend or member of my family with me as a 'minder', but to do this all of the time would obviously be too restrictive on them as well as me. When I am outside on my own, I carry a mobile-phone in my handbag just in case I need help.

I work on the counter of a charity shop and I stand at the till, usually with someone. There is an alarm button on the wall and if it is pushed in an emergency other staff members come to assist. However, most of the time, if I have a seizure at the counter the alarm is not needed. On one occasion I had a warning that a seizure was just about to take place in about five seconds, so I quickly put myself on the floor. The next thing I remember is seeing one of the other assistants smiling at me and saying: "let me get you some lemonade, dear". That afternoon was completed by a taxi bringing me home. The taxi drivers all know me, and know how forgetful I can be when I am ill, so they are always reminding me to put my seat belt on before starting off.

Back at home, I might do some gardening. I always ensure I do not use electrical tools and I find shears are probably the safest bet for cutting. Weeding and watering are quite safe.

Preparing the evening meal really has to be thought about. I prepare the meal but never start cooking it until there is someone else in the house. It is safer to use a peeler for potatoes, but I have not followed this policy on every occasion and must admit sometimes to using a knife. I prepare all of the vegetables and put them in their pans. If I want to fry I use a deep sided pan rather than a frying pan. I also make sure the water in the saucepans are not too full. The most important thing I do when I cook is to turn all of the pan handles towards the sides of the cooker. This is to make sure that I won't take a pan of boiling hot water down with me if I have a fall. I stand well back from the cooker when the stove is on, trying hard not to have the gases on 'high'. The meal may take longer to cook but really it is for the best. The hard work over, it is now time to enjoy it. I chew each mouthful well before swallowing it because choking can occur in some seizures.

At the end of the day when we go upstairs to bed my husband follows me up the stairs so he can catch me if I fall. We do exactly the same in railway stations or shopping malls where there are escalators, or when using any form of steps in fact. I stand sideways on the escalator- just in case. Don't get me wrong I do carry on as independent a life as possible, but there have been several instances where help was definitely needed on escalators and stairs.

Every week I do the week's grocery shopping and my husband or a friend comes with me. It takes so long that I find it a bit of an ordeal. Sometimes I must go alone and I travel by taxi to the store, a massive supermarket, and ask at the customer service counter for someone to walk round with me. They are very helpful and understand the situation. I have had several falls and absences, and have knocked things off shelves, so the staff have got to know me and even call me Julie.

Sometimes other modes of transport have to be used, apart from cars and taxis. When my husband and I visit the National Hospital for Neurology in central London we use the train and underground. The main thing I must remember is to stand well back from the edge whilst waiting on the platform. I need a 'minder' as the pressure and stress of the day really does mean I need one. There is pushing and shoving on the pavements and stations, and in the crowded trains and tubes, so I find it very difficult to manage on my own.

One thing I have learnt is to do things safely. If I need help, I try never to be afraid to ask for it.

10 Feelings from then to now

Most people are not actually biased against me, but I have always sensed them being impatient with me, especially when I was young.

At school, I would frequently black out for just a few seconds which was not obvious to the teacher, and I used to hate to ask her to repeat what she had said. As a result I would miss out on bits of the day.

Some people would not worry about my safety if a seizure took place, but they would be embarrassed at the fuss it caused.

One thing that did upset me as a child was the fact that I was fat. I do not know whether this was the medication or whether I ate all the wrong foods. I was called 'Fattie Arbuckle', and other similar nasty names and many times I would cry in bed as a result. I used to say to myself that they were teasing me because I was fat and not because I have epilepsy and happen to convulse sometimes. Anyone can be teased because they are fat - in a way it made me one of the 'gang'. I used to cherish this thought and it certainly helped me on the bad days.

I certainly used to think there was a difference between the young and the old people around me. Even now, many years on, I spend a lot of time with young people, and this has been so, throughout my life. For some reason children cope with my seizures and are not afraid.

Although my parents were very over-protective, they rarely talked about my condition. It was not something that was discussed and I wanted to talk about it on many, many occasions from when I first realised what the problem was. I saw it as nothing to hide. I can't speak for everyone, but certainly in my case I was frightened so there was a definite need to talk. Every Friday afternoon I saw a Consultant at the local hospital but although he was a very nice man he seemed to explain everything to my mother, rather than put it in simple terms for my benefit.

As a child, I did a lot, everything from puppet shows for my dolls to sailing. However, this was always accompanied by my mother reminding me to take my pills, to be careful when I crossed roads and to make sure I wore my life-jacket when sailing. All these things I took to be common sense.

My mother wanted me to wear dark glasses when I went to the local disco. I must admit that this made me feel stupid and different, not blending in with the crowd, so sometimes I would not wear them. I didn't know whether I suffered with photo-sensitive epilepsy then - no-one had told me and it was always just assumed that there was a risk. I never collapsed in the disco although sometimes I felt a little unwell, so I would take the glasses off. In fact, I never had any form of any seizure in a dance hall. I now realise that only a small proportion of epilepsy sufferers have their seizures triggered by flashing lights, and I am not one of them.

I felt I tried my best to work hard and play hard at school, enjoying both. However, I was always a bit nervous, insecure, and very shy. I had no confidence or self-esteem and I didn't even like myself. The nervousness and lack of confidence have faded over the years, but I still have that feeling of doubting myself. It is not something that can be easily overcome. I have spoken to many people who have a variety of serious illnesses or conditions, and they all report having a similar feeling. For someone with epilepsy perhaps the feeling is stronger. It is really easy to feel small and have doubts about yourself if you convulse on a pavement, give a blood curdling scream just before falling or perhaps urinate at the same time. I know I do.

During my later teenage years, I wanted to create my own family - to have children. My feelings for this grew so strong that I made the mistake of getting married, at eighteen, to a cruel man. So now I had the feelings of insecurity from a failed marriage plus the existing nervous feelings. For a long time after that I regarded myself as a second rate citizen.

Even now, some thirty years later, these 'down' feelings reappear from time to time. On most days the 'good' feelings surpass the 'bad' ones and these are the ones I cherish and nurture. It is really only when large seizures occur that the problems begin again.

I still have a terrible feeling of insecurity when I venture outside, regardless whether I have someone with me. I am never sure whether to take the risk or not. Each epilepsy sufferer will have to take this decision and it is totally up to the individual. I may feel fine and therefore able to go out but the seizures just happen - out of the blue - so it is difficult to predict when I am at risk.

I make a point of enjoying every day and every second without seizures. This has come to be part of a way of life over the years, and shall remain so. It is very important to have positive feelings about yourself. After a seizure, I not only pick myself up physically, but also mentally as well. Feelings vary from person to person, but my own feelings have been to avoid epilepsy being the be-all and end-all of my life. There are many wonderful things to do and see out there, all just waiting to be tried. So I try them, from simple everyday chores to a hot air balloon flight. I have found that it doesn't matter what it is. What is important is that you achieve it and put another 'notch on your belt'. On the days when all the bad feelings start to take over, I have to remember that there is another day tomorrow and that will be a lot better, so I look forward to that and many more to follow.

11

The good life

From a very young age I could enjoy life but only to a certain extent. When I was just ten, I loved fairs, roundabouts and swings, in fact anything that was fun. The trouble was that my mother did not like me to go on the faster rides, which she felt might be dangerous for me, so I could only look longingly at the big wheel and the cars. I think my mother believed that the seizures would occur on the rides, and she was always careful. One of the very few rides she said was all right for me to use was the one with the 'up and down horses' which was relatively slow. I remember regularly going into the amusement park near to my home, and for the most part I heeded my mother's warnings. I didn't go on any fast rides even when I was with my friends, but I did stretch a point with the 'dodgem' cars and would go on these quite regularly. I used to go in the 'penny arcades', another place my mother was not keen on me going. Was this because of all the flashing lights of the fruit machines, or was it because there were 'undesirables' in there? I have never been sure. I was one of the children that spent a lot of time on the stands, the coconut shies and the like, things that my mother felt were safe for me. I did feel as though I missed out on all the water shoots, big wheels and so on. Despite yearning for them I realised it was probably for the best.

These restrictions did not stop me from enjoying my childhood to the full and I loved to play all of the sports at school. I remember being 'lethal' with a hockey stick, learning how to use it as a hook, and trip other girls up for a joke. Fortunately they, too found it funny. I did a lot of sports, none of which I am proud to say were affected by my epilepsy.

It was a few years later that I really noticed that I was different. I would go out with my friends in the evening, and like all teenagers they thought it clever to drink heavily. The only problem was that alcohol reacted with my anti-epileptic medication. I used to find myself very ill, but I thought it was all right to continue drinking because everybody was doing it. My head would be swimming, everything would appear bent and distorted and the room would go round and round. Then I would usually fall and would become unconscious. Then I realised, this wasn't a good time, and was just being stupid. It was at this stage I started to realise having a good time was about enjoying yourself rather than impressing others. I started drinking diet coke at the pub. No-one remarked on this. They, too had finally realised that I was unable to take alcoholic drinks, and they realised that this was a sensible and mature decision.

To enjoy life to the full with any disability you have to be very much an individual, and be able to resist peer pressure. This does not mean you cannot enjoy parties and the pranks and games we all play in our youth. I lived by the sea when I was young, and after a good time we would throw someone off the slip-way then all dive in after them. I remember this being fun. I used to love to dance at parties and would sometimes spend all night just dancing. I would get hot and sticky but I would enjoy every last minute. Having epilepsy did not seem to get in the way of all that.

In my youth, I made sure I travelled around Britain and, on other occasions, abroad. At school I would go on school outings to France. I enjoyed the feeling of being on a boat and the challenge of trying to make myself understood in French. I would have little absences on these wonderful days, but I didn't worry so neither did anybody else.

When I was fourteen, my mother took me on a two week Mediterranean cruise. Amongst the wonderful places we visited were Split, Corfu, Dubrovnik, Malta and Tunisia. It really was a special time. On one occasion a whirlwind hit us, which was quite nasty. When you are young, though, nothing seems to matter and I was partying and enjoying the company, the music and the surroundings. The places were beautiful and I was free of major seizures. It was hot and steamy, perhaps a little too hot, but the joy for me was seeing different cultures and local people going about their everyday business. I wanted to learn from that. It was noticeable, though, that I had more absences in the heat, and this is something I have always found. However, these couldn't spoil the good times, they were just too good to miss. I thoroughly enjoyed sitting on deck drinking what I pretended to be wine, though it was in fact lemonade. The pool shimmered in the bright sunlight, and when the heat from the sun would gradually warm the water it was like diving into a bath.

More recently, I have had many wonderful days out, all of which were special. Two that stand out are the VE Day Anniversary celebrations in Hyde Park in 1995, and visiting the Millennium Dome in 2000. Both of these places were full of people and this meant that we had to be especially careful. The pushing and shoving of crowds make me more stressed, and this can lead to seizures which can be even more hazardous in a crowded place. I got through both days admirably with only long absences or just the little flicker that seemed to last for a split second. Going to London has always been exciting event for me, there is always so much to see and do and the memory of these days will stay with me a long time.

The Millennium Dome was fantastic and I thoroughly enjoyed it. There was so much to see and do - from old fashioned entertainers walking on stilts, to great big displays that you walked around - that it would have been impossible to experience everything. There was so much information to take in that I thought my mind would explode. My husband kept watching me every minute of the time just to check that I was all right. I held onto his arm for extra support just in case I needed it. We took the day at our own pace not rushing round like some. We knew we would both enjoy it more if no larger seizures occurred.

When we went to the VE Day 50th Anniversary in London's Hyde Park, it was a very hot day and there were occasions when I felt quite ill. I had to sit down several times because of the 'swimming' sensation in my head, but the heat wasn't going to spoil the day. It was a day of celebrating victory, and it was going to be a victory for me too.

For many years I avoided going to the cinema and the theatre, but within the past few years I am proud to say I have visited both. My husband and I were always a bit cautious just in case I had a major seizure which would be so noisy that it would spoil other people's enjoyment. And we could imagine the upheaval at a live performance if I were to collapse noisily. In recent years, my medication has had the effect of reducing the noise of seizures so we felt able to risk going to see a film whilst on holiday. This was so successful that we thought we would try to see a stage play. Beforehand, we had a meal out and my nerves gradually started to build up. However, all of my fears were unfounded as I did not have a seizure. We have since been to several movies and plays without incident, but we keep our fingers crossed each time.

I have always loved seaside outings and I went to Brighton on a 'works outing' with my husband and his colleagues. This was another good day and again it was hot. Whilst playing ten pin bowling my husband noticed that I had blacked out for a few seconds on the aisle, and came to my rescue, never embarrassed or upset, just taking it as a matter of course. He never makes excuses or tries to apologise for my 'strange' behaviour, he accepted it a long time ago. This is why I am able to enjoy these wonderful days - whatever happens I needn't worry. After the bowling we enjoyed a meal and walked round all the narrow back roads and on the pier.

Despite having black spots, I enjoyed the day as much as any body else.

Folkestone is somewhere else we visit frequently. I was born there and my mother still lives there. I love to go down and watch the boats sailing around the bay.

Three or four times a year we travel to our holiday home in Pembrokeshire, South-west Wales, and visit my husband's family at the same time. The long car journey sometimes takes its toll on me, and I am not well for a day or two, after which I am ready to enjoy the holiday. It is very quiet in Pembrokeshire, compared to where we live in Hertfordshire, the lifestyle is totally different. There are beaches which we can laze on or beautiful country walks if we want to be a little more active. The trips down there are worth it if only for the scenery.

One thing I am often asked about is flying. Many years ago, I flew to Northern Ireland to visit relatives. My brother and I were flying as unaccompanied children. The airline staff were told about my epilepsy and they proved to be very helpful, offering me drinks and things to eat, which made me feel very important. I was concerned that the changing air pressure might lead to a seizure, but it did not seem to have any effect other than that my ears 'popped' as everyone else's did. I was fine for the rest of the journey, so I think I can safely say that I am all right in an aeroplane. Recently, I have been up in a hot air balloon and had a helicopter trip over London, but more of that later.

These are all prime-times that I enjoyed, savoured and experienced without it being diluted by my having epilepsy. It is a question of being careful and knowing your limits. Once you can achieve this, it is possible to enjoy and savour life in the same way as anyone else.

12   Overcoming depression, panic and psychosis

I s my state of mind affected by my condition? The answer to this is a difficult one. Mental health varies from person to person. And an individual's mental state changes from time to time. Not everyone with a physical disability has poor mental health, and not everyone who is mentally ill is physically disabled. However, in my case I think my physical condition has played a large part in my state of mind.

For me there are many good days. but sometimes it is all too easy to let the bad days overshadow the good ones. Slowly my heart and soul start to sink, tears start to fall and bit by bit, day by day I begin to feel useless. If the seizures are regular, going out of the house becomes a major step, so I am stuck indoors feeling sorry for myself, thinking that epilepsy is a major part of my life.

This was exactly how I felt several years ago. I stayed close to the house, rarely venturing out. Fortunately, my family and friends were strong and encouraged me to go out. At first I would go out only when accompanied by a 'minder', usually a close friend or a family member. To begin with, we would go to the local shops. This involved crossing a main road, so I would always cross with someone. I gradually worked my way up to the big supermarket at the other end of town, again I was with someone, but I had started to go out.

I came to the conclusion that by staying indoors most of the time my mental health was being badly affected. I was nervous and having panic attacks, which would leave me shaking and grinding my hands. I had to start believing in myself and, above all, do something constructive with my life, rather than simply sitting there and worrying about the next seizure.

Writing my thoughts and feelings down on a scrap of paper helped me. All those deep inner thoughts - how I felt about epilepsy and how I felt it prevented me from doing things - had finally come out . I started writing short articles, purely for my own satisfaction, and I found it helpful to read and re-read them. Then a friend encouraged me to send them to women's magazines. It took a lot of persuasion by her as I thought people would be totally disinterested in what I had to say. However, eventually we sent some off, and to my great surprise they were picked for publication. Two articles were published, one in

Woman and the other in Take a Break. I had finally discovered that I could do something on my own without a 'minder'. I started to write more and more, and several more articles were published.

Although I had a large stock of writings, only a few were sent for publication. I had a file full of short pieces about my life and everything to do with epilepsy, and wondered how I could best use them? Once again I was prompted by my husband and a friend. They suggested I contacted a little local school about speaking to the children on 'Living with Epilepsy'. My first thought was that they were joking but after a great deal of coaxing I eventually said I would give it a go.

I remember that day very well. I had dreaded it for several days in advance, even having nightmares. The children were about ten years old and everyone sat on tiny chairs - this included me! I had nowhere to put my legs! I was extremely frightened, but managed to do the talk. I stuttered. I stammered. I even had absences. I thought it was an absolute disaster. Afterwards the children clapped and cheered and I thought they were being polite. The teacher came up to me afterwards remarking on what a wonderful job I had done - despite the absences. She said she could tell that the children warmed to me immediately and loved the talk. I couldn't believe it They honestly didn't mind the fact I was having seizures. But I suppose, that was what the talk was all about wasn't it?

I gave the same talk to a few more schools and got a similar reaction from them all. This had killed two birds with one stone: I was finally opening up and talking about epilepsy, and at the same time informing people about the condition. Although I was still nervous, my confidence was building gradually and I had reached the stage where it did not matter to me whether I had seizures during a talk.

The talk was tried on the 'dreaded teens'. They, too, warmed to me and were most receptive so I went to more secondary schools. On one occasion I had a tonic clonic seizure whilst on the stage. The young people accepted it, and even helped me through the talk prompting me and being patient with me. I spoke to more and more schools becoming more confident each time. As I became more successful at it, the teachers would ask me back time and time again.

I began to realise that I could speak in other towns in the district, so I spread my wings a little and started talking to schools further and further afield. I was always accompanied by a friend for support and help. By now I had gained some confidence and that made me feel good.

I started to lecture to a variety of groups, after all it wasn't only schools that needed to be taught about epilepsy. I went to universities, the county police headquarters, shops and even hospitals, getting further and further afield over a range of several counties. And I was actually enjoying the experience.

I have had some tonic clonic seizures at lectures over the past three years but I came to accept them as part of my everyday life. If I appeared too ill, my hosts were often kind to offer to read the lecture for me from the notes I had brought with me. But I would not have it - I wanted to talk. I would always explain at the beginning of the talk that it was possible that a seizure might take place, so the audience would be prepared for it and accept me as I am.

Despite still having low days, my confidence grew to the extent that I decided it might be an idea to try to talk on the radio. I thought that it would be fun, but was concerned that I would have an absence on air, or even worse a major seizure? Once again, I decided not to make excuses for myself. I would be talking about epilepsy so they would have to appreciate that there was the possibility I might have a seizure. A few telephone calls later I had interested several local stations. Some interviewed me in a studio, and others on the phone. They didn't all go well. For instance, in the studio at Radio Essex I kept having small absences and this upset me, though the radio station did not seem to mind. I have now spoken to dozens of local radio stations across several counties, and these went without a hitch.

Talking to sixth-formers and their teacher about living with epilepsy

I started writing articles for more national and local publications. A friend suggested I tried to get on Carlton Television's public access programme, 'Your Shout'. I did not think that it would be chosen or that Carlton would interested in my script - but they were. They contacted me straight away and shortly afterwards filmed an interview with me working in the charity shop. The ten minute television programme was transmitted in 1999. I felt very proud of it.

Big hospitals, schools and shops were now asking me to speak. Everyone seemed interested and able to accept me as I am. It is amazing to think that all of this came from a scrap of paper and a few thoughts. Writing and talking about epilepsy has given me strength of character and, above all, dignity and self respect. It also gave me the enthusiasm to write this book. It doesn't matter what goal you choose to do, or what dreams are in the back of your mind, try to make them reality. Get on and do it.

A common problem with disabled people is loneliness and, like depression, it is very difficult to resolve. Able bodied people tell you to go out more, but what if you are unable to do so. What if the seizures are so regular that you begin to dread every moment of every day just in case another one comes along. The temptation is to stay indoors but this can lead to depression and loneliness and a feeling that there is not a lot that can be done about it.

I found that the solution was to enjoy my own company and not to look at the garden path, hoping someone would walk down it. At one time I was having six major seizures each week and thirty or forty absences each day. Obviously, going out was extremely difficult. These were the days when loneliness became a real problem. I was frightened to leave the house so I could not enjoy other people's company, and my family was at school or at work all day. I would sit for hours in the safety of a chair, or do housework. For company, I would listen to the radio or play CDs for hours on end. I would dance to the music which was turned up loud to dispel the quiet of the house. I would sing along, pretending to be Tina Turner or Cher, holding an imaginary microphone in my hand. The great thing about being alone is that you can do what you like as nobody can see you. If I felt like being a little quieter, I would sit and watch television for hours on end, usually chat shows such as Ricky Lake. I would join in the conversation about the people on the show, arguing for or against, and 'oohing and ahing' in the right places. Seizures occurred during the day and I would have to deal with them in the best way I could.

Another method of coping was to hold conversations with myself, or even talking to the cat from next door that frequented our front porch.

Nowadays, even though my epilepsy has improved, I talk to myself about the cleaning that needs doing in the house and the shopping I must get.

Dealing with everyday matters can be a trial. Five years ago, I became very frightened, almost to the point where I would not go out for fear of having a seizure. It developed into panic attacks every time I did. Those days where frightful. The shortness of breath, the panting, the swirling sensation that followed all became a part of me that I had to deal with. The panic attacks became a daily occurrence, and I had them even if I did not go out. It got to the stage where the slightest thing could spark one off.

At about the same time, I started to experience another uncomfortable effect. I would stare at an object and my brain would pick out all the pieces that were coloured black. Eventually, my mind was telling me that everything was black. It could be something as small as a stone or the black in someone's eye, it really didn't matter. It made me feel very hot and very sick.

I was recommended to see a 'behavioural therapist' at the National Hospital for Neurology. She was a nice lady who had a calming effect on me. Her voice was quiet, I remember. She told me that she thought both problems were based on panic attacks, and set about teaching me how to manage them. To counteract the panting, I had to practice deep breathing - in through the nose and out through the mouth. Another technique was to sit on a comfortable chair, close my eyes and think nice thoughts. I chose to imagine calming seas and sailing boats. The concentration on all things black was treated by my concentrating on things that were colourful. I tended to dress in black a lot, so I started to wear brighter, richer colours, and this helped.

These conditions still linger to the present day but, thanks to the therapist, I have learnt how to control them.

Another problem I encounter from time to time involves strange - even bizarre - thoughts. For instance, that my heart has stopped beating, or even that I am dying. Or that one side of my body feels like a lump of jelly. Sometimes this psychosis can last for a few days, other times it can last for several months. They can feel very real, and I can take some convincing that they are not true. These episodes put a strain on my family. The feelings are also very uncomfortable indeed for me and sometimes lead to depression. I now take a drug which reduces these thoughts to a minimum. Every time they return. I temporarily increase the dose of tablets and within a few days I am fine. What must be realised is that the brain is a wondrous piece of machinery. It is not surprising that a piece 'shuts down' from time to time. A doctor has recently suggested that these episodes are connected with changes in the nature of my epilepsy.

In order to live with a disability, the right state of mind is essential. It is important to think positively. Life can be enjoyed by doing what is possible, whenever it is possible, and not being constrained by too many self-imposed boundaries. I have found that setting my sights too low can be worse than overdoing things.

13

Confidence and self-esteem

Confidence and self-esteem follow naturally from a belief in one-self. Acquiring this self-belief takes different amounts of time for different people.

My own self-belief is a lot better than when I was younger, but even now it is not overflowing. This is only partly to do with the fact that I have epilepsy. In fact, many people who have serious seizures still manage to have high levels of confidence and self-esteem.

Of course anyone's confidence would be inclined to take a bit of a knock when seizures occur. This is especially the case in front of a staring crowd, most of them not knowing what to do or even what is going on. Afterwards, when I come to, I have to pick myself up off the floor and somehow hold my head high. My family always tell me never to apologise to the crowd, something I am inclined to do.

It is possible to have very little confidence but still send out 'messages' to others that you are in fact brimming over with it. It was more difficult in my teenage years to do this, but everything is difficult at that very special time. These days I put up a 'front'. Then when the real confidence and self-esteem has grown it can take over from the facade.

I was unsure of myself as a child, but friends and neighbours, would always give me the zest I needed to fight another day. My friends' positive attitude made the bad times easier and gave me the confidence to cope. In later years when I held down a job, I am proud to say that all my employers were very pleased with me and their original doubts in me were dispelled. I managed to prove that, despite my disability, I could do the job as well as anyone could. The real confidence and self esteem was not there. It was my 'front' showing people I could do what was needed.

My self-esteem received a boost when I had two children who proved to be free of any condition or ailment. At that point I realised I was capable of doing the same task as most women - have children. It really did boost my morale, especially when there were people advising me against it.

It is not always easy to believe in yourself. It takes a while to be able to say "I can" rather than " I can't". It also takes effort and a great deal of strength. The turning point for me was when I decided that everything was possible, and that I was determined to enjoy life to the full and not to be ashamed of my condition any longer. It was only a few years ago that this happened.

I took on voluntary work and this gave me a sense of pride that I was achieving something for the community. I have confidence in this work. To start with I made mistakes and even wondered whether I would ever be able to master the job. It was not a difficult job, working with the public and working on a till, but pressing all the right keys and remembering to give the right change seemed an awful lot to do. After practice, I became genuinely confident and no longer needed to put on a show. Now I know the job so well that it is like second nature to me. I am able to hold my head high and experience the pleasures of feeling good about myself. To achieve this is marvellous.

I never believed I would be able to lecture about my condition. The thought seemed daunting. I would be nervous sometimes for anything up to two months beforehand. I would tremble for days before the talk. And when I started the talk, I would stutter and shudder, but this would only last for a few minutes, then I would get under steam and have no problem delivering the lecture. It is quite normal for anyone appearing in public to feel nervous initially, and then to get a flush of adrenaline. So what may seem to be the result of a lack of confidence is all perfectly normal and will go. Afterwards, there is a wonderful feeling of achievement. This is caused by a body chemical called dopamine. This, too, can last several days. At this stage, I feel like jumping in the air and even dancing, and this feeling comes after every lecture.

My confidence tends to build because of that wonderful feeling which is second to none. A feeling of being needed or wanted, and also knowing what to do. I simply say to myself: "I can do it" and I am able to lecture to crowds or make a cup of coffee, whatever it is I am trying to achieve. When I feel like this, a sudden seizure will not spoil the day.

I have always managed to carry on my lecture following a seizure. I have collapsed twice during my talks and once whilst on the way to one. Being able to pick myself up again requires a positive state of mind. On these occasions, the talks I gave were not as good as usual, but I had come to explain epilepsy and I was determined to do just that. Determination goes hand in hand with confidence. If you have the one, you can generally say you will have the other.

When I am on my own, my self esteem and confidence seems to wither away. Why is this, I wonder? I think it is probably because I start to become very introverted and wrapped up in my own thoughts. It is very important, especially when you are on your own to be able to develop a way of occupying your brain. It doesn't matter what you do: reading, writing, computer work even watching television. It gives the brain something to deal with other than negative thoughts.

Some epilepsy sufferers are embarrassed and upset if they have a seizure in front of members of the public who may be staring and pointing. It is easy to believe that people are laughing at this person on the ground. The chances are they are not, they are merely at a loss to know what to do. Once it is possible to get over this stage of being upset with your own seizures you are well on the way to feeling confident. To be able literally to pick yourself off the ground takes some doing. To be able to smile at your 'audience' whilst doing so also takes some doing. Although it is most difficult for someone newly diagnosed with epilepsy to find confidence, believe me this ability does come eventually.

Quite often the sufferer will feel that their family is ashamed and embarrassed by their seizures. I know I feel this way sometimes, but I look them in the face and ask myself whether I think they are really embarrassed. Usually I conclude that they are not.

Because I had little confidence, I used to stare at the floor when speaking to people. One of the most helpful ways I found to overcome this was to look in the mirror and hold a conversation with myself. Now I look people in the eye. I also watched my posture, making sure I walked with my head held high at all times. I decided to make myself feel good by putting on nice clothes every day, whether I was going out or not, and this really boosted my ego. It was something that I could enjoy both physically and mentally. Loving yourself is a trick that everyone should be able to do.

Epilepsy is a condition like no other because you never know when a seizure will happen. There is always uncertainty which gives rise to feelings of insecurity. My way of coping is by believing that the next day must be tackled, whether I am seizure free or not. I try to try to think positive thoughts and live each day as if I am going to enjoy it. Confidence and self esteem follows naturally from this.

14   Ten unforgettable moments

There are several occasions that for some reason or another stand out as having being special because of other peoples actions. They are not goals or ambitions, just moments made memorable for one reason or another. Here are ten of my favourites:

Caught in the act

One day whilst working in the charity shop, one of the customers asked me to fetch a box full of valuable crockery for her. I did so, then suddenly a swimming sensation went through my head. I remember seeing a vague impression of my colleagues face and quickly held out my arms for her to take the box, then there was nothing but blackness. I landed in the arms of the customer. It wasn't a long seizure, just a few minutes, and I quickly recovered. It was a hot day that day and I could feel the lady's wet sweaty arms against me as I started to regain consciousness. She had caught me and I was grateful. My safety seemed to be her top priority and she did not leave my side until after she could make sense of what I was saying. She didn't seem the slightest bit concerned for her crockery, - just concerned for me. It just goes to show how kind and selfless some people can be. This could well have been a lifesaving act, and it left me feeling particularly grateful.

I hold up a Post Office

My second 'moment', on the other hand , shows what people can be like at their worst - without them even realising it. I was in the local Post Office, waiting in a very long queue that seemed to take ages to move. Everyone in the queue was getting fed up. It came to my turn and an absence occurred lasting several seconds. The little old lady queuing behind me was getting impatient and was (I was told later) grumbling that I had not moved up to the counter. I stood there with my head quivering slightly. She looked at my face and must have seen my eyes fluttering, then proceeded to poke me with her fingers in my arms, back and side. She apparently became more and more irritated that I had not moved.

The Postmaster knew me and saw what had happened. Instead of serving other customers, including the old lady, he came out from behind the counter with a chair, and did not say a word to the lady. He took his time sitting me down in front of the counter whilst the queue was getting longer and longer. The Postmaster had realised that I would regain consciousness in a few seconds, which is exactly what happened. I got my bearings, got up from the chair and was served next in the queue. The old lady could not wait a minute or two and was still mumbling underneath her breath. As I have learnt, the best thing to do in these circumstances, is to ignore stupid animosity.

Ready, aim, fire!

This has to be one of my favourites albeit a long time ago when my brother would teach me his boyish ways. The one thing he and I used to love was his air-rifle. My mother would drive into the countryside with us on a Sunday afternoon. My mother and I would pick bluebells and primroses whilst my brother did target practice with his gun. Then came the big day. My brother taught me how to use his air-rifle. I couldn't have been more than nine or ten. He showed how to line up the sights, then we put targets on a nearby tree and we would shoot for hours. It was great fun. I cannot say I was a great shot like my brother who used to get 'bulls' very frequently. I would hit the target, but not quite so near the bull. He tried for hours teaching me. Sometimes we would put a target on the garden shed and my brother, two of his friends and I would fire air-pellets at it. They were truly days when I was a tom boy.

The reason this was so special to me was that my brother trusted me to do something that others may well have prohibited. He knew that, with care and proper supervision, it was possible for me to do anything I wanted, without it being dangerous to me or others.

The crinoline lady

I loved to reward the local children for all the help and encouragement they gave me when my sons were very young. I did this by making cakes and decorating them in special ways. On one particular occasion I discovered that one of the little girls who came to visit me would love a cake shaped like a crinoline lady. I spoke to her mother about it without her knowledge and she thought it would be a wonderful idea.

I had seen the design in a cookery book, but it was one of the more difficult ones. In fact I doubted whether I would be skilled enough, but I was determined to give it a try. "Surely it couldn't be that difficult", I remember thinking to myself. I planned ages in advance, and made myself quite ill as a result. I was worried whether all would be well and

this of course is stressful. The cake was to be centred on a real doll, and the girl's mother smuggled one of her favourite dolls into my kitchen. I made the cake, and cut it into a dome shape, than placed the doll in the centre so that the dome formed the 'hoops' of the dress. Icing it took hours of patience over a period of two days. The intricate shapes were very fiddly and it was difficult to get the colours right.

Eventually it was finished, despite me having several seizures of varying degrees. I was proud of myself. She looked really lovely. A great deal of thought, time and work had gone into this cake, but the reaction of the little girl was second to none. "Did you do this for me, Julie?", she said. Her face beamed. She would have known that the job would not have been easy for me, but she knew I liked a challenge. This was truly a moment to savour. And we enjoyed eating the cake, too.

Going with the flow

This must be one of my favourite memories. It is all about a place I feel safe in. Somewhere I felt most at home - the sea. For some reason, no seizures have ever occurred in sea water. I would spend hours of my youth on it, in it and beside it. One thing I loved to do was to swim underwater, underneath the jellyfish, looking up at their tentacles. They looked lovely, simply going with the flow of water around them. I would try hard not to get stung, and never was. Like most young people, I enjoyed the thrill that comes from doing something dangerous. I used to swim right underneath the centreboard of my sailing boat and would surface quite happily on the other side, gasping for breath but enjoying every minute of it. I would also dive from the beach through the large, powerful breakers that use to hit the shore. Sometimes I would surf the breakers but I was useless at that! I would fall off every time, but I still loved it. I had a lot of confidence whilst in the sea which was a home from home, somewhere I could always be safe. I did, and still do, love the sea. It has its angry days, but then so does everybody. Like a young child, it is entitled to throw a tantrum every now and again. [Note that the sea must be treated as a potentially dangerous place, and other disabled people may not find it as safe as I did].

Broomstick and cauldron

When I first started to do my talks, I needed something to give them an 'edge'. Something that the children in the schools could find amusing and therefore realise I was not a prim and proper 'old' lady. So I came up with the idea of dressing as a witch. Hundreds of years ago, people with epilepsy were thought to be possessed by evil spirits and would be burnt at the stake as witches. I was very nervous the first time I tried this, not knowing quite what the children would think. I entered the hall wearing a cloak, a witch's hat over a black wig, and carrying a broomstick and cauldron. I was quoting from Macbeth: "when shall we three meet again. In thunder, lighting, or in rain?"

They all looked dumbfounded. The atmosphere was electric. Their faces where full of expectation and delight. They started to giggle and challenged me, saying: "it's not Halloween miss" and "do you fly, too". All sorts of comments came out. It was marvellous. My fears had been totally unfounded. Their laughter, merriment and enjoyment was second to none. I found they listened far more attentively and actually took an interest in what I was saying. I explained how witches were

relevant to epilepsy, then took the costume off and demonstrated that underneath was a normal human being, looking no different to anyone else. The whole idea had been well worth it.

I don't think I shall ever forget the expression on their faces when I walked into that room. The same idea worked time and time again in different schools and getting a similar reaction means the idea was a success. To be honest, I think I enjoyed it as much as the children. A local newspaper printed a photograph of me dressed up in my costume, and this attracted much local interest. My friends and colleagues loved it. This is definitely a moment I shall always treasure.

Weathering the Storms - living with epilepsy

An itch in time

My brother and I had a holiday in Northern Ireland when I was aged about nine, staying with my uncle and aunt. We enjoyed the holiday very much but wanted to get back to family and friends. Unfortunately, we went down with chicken pox so we were quarantined for several weeks and not allowed to fly back home. We both felt extremely sorry for ourselves as we had to stay indoors, and as my uncle and aunt did not have children there was very little to do.

It was very interesting to note that although I felt very ill and was suffering the stress of being forcibly absent from home, there was no increase in my seizures. I spent the days composing short stories on my uncle's typewriter. He was a journalist by profession and he told me he enjoyed reading my stories. It was his encouragement all those years ago that gave me the confidence to write articles later in life, and ultimately this book.

Carnival time

Everyone should have a moment when they feel important - 'the cat's whiskers'. For me this was carnival day in Folkestone. I was a member of a local yacht club and they would always enter a float in the carnival which was the envy of many surrounding towns. The rescue boat, a large rubber dinghy with an outboard engine, would be towed on a trailer behind a truck. We would all dress up in our sailing gear - lifejackets, jeans, waterproofs - and sit on board the boat, laughing about anything and everything, eating and drinking shandy or fizzy pop, all the time going around the streets of Folkestone waving at the crowds and encouraging them to throw money at us for the charity collection. It was quite an exciting time. I would feel important and part of the team and, what's more, that team needed me. After the carnival had finished, we were still having fun and this usually resulted in someone being thrown off the slipway into the sea. The evening would end with a party and I always felt I was one of the crowd and not at all discriminated against.

Long hot summers

The high spot of being a mother was when my children were young. I remember some hot steamy days when we would get out the big paddling pool and fill it calf high with water. Then my boys and I, and all the local children, would have water fights in the garden with the hose. We used the excuse that we were watering the plants, but it wasn't just the plants that got soaked; everything did including the side of the house! As the soil was clay, the lawn would become a mud pit but we would all really enjoy ourselves! The local children were very young but they had no worries about me and treated me as a normal person able to enjoy myself, even if it did mean I got muddy. These children were always kind and even now I get Christmas cards and letters from some of them, twenty years on. I shall never forget them or those long hot days.

Room with a loo

My conservatory was built onto the house about four years ago. My husband had the brilliant idea of adding a downstairs toilet at the same time. It gave me a wonderful feeling of safety. I could go the whole day without having to manage the dreadful stairs to get to the toilet. I have had so many seizures on the stairs and many nasty falls, resulting in everything from cuts and bruises to broken ribs and nose. It has been a boon ever since it was built. I now have a tremendous feeling of safety and increased independence, and no longer have to shout out "I'm going upstairs". I can sit in the conservatory on the cooler days or with the sunshine shining on me, and take in the love-ly surroundings. It is large and allows me extra space to move around in. I can enjoy the outside, yet be safely inside if I want to be.

15   Twenty questions I am often asked

I am asked many questions about my condition, some out of curiosity and others out of ignorance. I am constantly surprised at how little is generally known about epilepsy and this is one of the reasons that I lecture to schools and colleges trying hard to obliterate this ignorance. Below are some of the favourite questions that people ask me.

Was it difficult having children?

I gave birth in the same way as any other woman. My husband was there calming me down and mopping my brow. Extra nurses were on hand just in case a seizure should happen during childbirth. However, I knew I could do it without a problem and that thought is what kept me going. I always wanted children, and for my husband and I they were wonderful moments when our sons were born.

We realised it would be hard work in the future, but we would prove wrong all of those people who had said I should adopt, and who obviously had no idea about the condition. My sons are now grown up but are still a joy to me.

Was it hard forming relationships?

This is difficult to answer. Where boys were concerned, I was always a good friend to them, though not much more. In my early teens, I was extremely fat and not very pretty, and boys always looked on me as one of the gang instead of a girlfriend. I don't think this had anything to do with the fact that I had epilepsy. By the time I reached sixteen I started to wear makeup and dress less like a tomboy, and I did have a boyfriend. Unlike those of most of my friends, my relationships always lasted for several months to a year. My friends seemed to spend the odd week with one boyfriend then move on. Perhaps it was because I needed that extra stability to help me.

A successful relationship with family, friends or colleagues depends very much upon the person. If they have the right attitude towards epilepsy and do not see it as an insurmountable object, a good relationship can be enjoyed. The situation is always helped by my friendly disposition and my honesty in explaining about my condition at an early stage.

Were you ever tempted to smoke and drink?

I smoked very heavily for a long time, but now I don't smoke at all. As a comfort, I hold a real cigarette but never light it. I started smoking from a very young age. At the age of twelve, I had one a day then gradually worked up to a 50-a-day chain-smoking habit by the time I was twenty. This resulted in the usual chesty cough and difficult breathing, but I did find smoking to have a calming effect. However it did not do the rest of my body any good and I gave up smoking when I reached forty. I did this with the help of nicotine patches and immediately felt better, and richer, for having done so. It also gave me a great sense of achievement to have kicked a long-standing addiction.

As for drinking, it is not advisable to take alcoholic drinks whilst on anti-convulsant medication. But of course, when I was a teenager I did not listen to such good advice. I wanted to be the same as anybody else, so I just carried on. As a rule, drink and medicine do not mix and I was either violently sick or else felt as though I was on the ceiling. In my teenage years I drunk too much, and did it simply to prove that I could. As I got older the effects would become obvious. Sometimes I would go to a party and have just three glasses of wine, but then I would have to be taken home. Nowadays, I do have the odd glass of wine but try to keep it at that. I go to parties and hold onto the same glass all evening, just sipping from it every now and again, and nobody notices. In a phrase, I have grown up.

Did you like to stay up late at night in the past, or even now?

Any young person likes to stay up late at night. From when I was ten or so, I wanted to stay up. My mother, however, was not always happy to let me do this. It was thought that epilepsy would be reduced by having lots of sleep, so I always had to go to bed much earlier than my friends. When I reached my teenage years and attended discos, my mother wanted me to get home early. Like most young people I had a mind of my own and disobeyed my mother many times to stay up late. The father of one of my friends was a teacher and 'looked after' the school's video recorder - this was before every house had one - and after a disco, a group of us would watch videos until the early hours. Sometimes I was indeed ill, and this could have been connected with the late nights, but the thing with epilepsy is that nothing is sure. Now, thirty years on, I find I need more sleep. Sometimes I find I am so dopey because of the medication I take that I cannot watch the end of a television programme before falling asleep on the sofa.

Weathering the Storms - living with epilepsy

What about fast rides and roundabouts at the funfair?

These were always forbidden. My mother said that they were not very stable, but I suspect that it was because she was terrified in case I would have a seizure and fall whilst I was on it. I had to content myself with the 'up and down horses' (that's me in the picture) because it was a slow ride, and this was about all I was allowed to do. From a very early age I realised my mother was being very pro-

tective of me. Sometimes I used to get fed up with it, but I suppose she had my best interests at heart, and I still avoid fast fairground rides to this day.

Do you have a problem going on holiday?

It really depends on where I want to go. I have travelled abroad, visiting various European and North African countries on a cruise round the Mediterranean. I have been to Ireland and worked in Spain. But this was mainly when I was a teenager, at a time when my epilepsy was not nearly so bad as it is now.

As I got older it became more difficult to travel abroad especially to non-English-speaking countries. If I were to have a seizure in the street, it really could prove to be quite a difficult situation - it is bad enough in this country! Medical insurance for holidays abroad could also be costly. So now we holiday in the United Kingdom. My husband has family in Wales so we spend some of our time there. We have also toured parts of Scotland, the Lake District, the Norfolk Broads and Cornwall. It is often advisable to alert hotel staff to the possibility of a seizure happening, so they know not to worry if I collapse. People in catering have usually come across all sorts of illnesses and are rarely upset by epilepsy.

Although I enjoy our British holidays, I look forward to my seizures becoming sufficiently controlled that I can once more go abroad.

Because your seizures are frequent, can you go out alone?

Although on most of my trips out I am accompanied by family and friends, there are times when I have to (or want to) venture out alone. This is something that needs confidence and this takes time to build up. There was a stage in my life when I would never leave the house and would be on my own for hours. However, my family convinced me that seizures would occur whether I was in the house or not, and the advantage of being outside is there are usually people around. Gradually I built up enough confidence to leave the house on my own. It took a lot of time, and even now my heart flutters when I cross a road. I remind myself that life goes on and nothing I can do will stop the seizures.

Do you ever feel embarrassed about having seizures?

I am not embarrassed as such. I have never felt embarrassed about having epilepsy, and can talk to anybody about it without feeling self-conscious. However, sometimes I have a major seizure whilst in the company of strangers and I will feel rather silly afterwards. I think I am concerned about what they may be thinking about the situation. My friends and family have grown to accept the seizures as part of me so they are not embarrassed. Some people do get embarrassed when I collapse but I regard it as their problem, not mine. Whilst in my early teens I used to feel embarrassed about my seizures but I have become more confident since then. My husband and sons have taught me to hold my head high, and thanks to them I do just that.

Why don't you go out to work? If you do a voluntary job your health can't be that bad.

Several people have asked me this. For most people with epilepsy, full time employment is not a problem. In my case, however, my seizures are very poorly controlled by my medication, so I am unable to give the commitment that paid work requires. I can never guarantee on a day to day basis that I will be well enough to work. In fact, I do not know from one hour to the next how good or bad my health will be. A voluntary job gives you a bit of pride, self-respect, and a feeling that you are doing something useful with your life, whilst not requiring a rigid attendance pattern. On the days I am able to work I am there for a few hours, but it is enough to be able to hold my head high in the community. With a voluntary job, many of the pressures of work are still there but I can choose the level of pressure.

An absence lasts only a few seconds, so it's trivial, isn't it?

This was said to me just recently and I nearly lost my temper. An absence may not be as dramatic as a major seizure, and usually there is no fall involved, but injuries incurred can be just as bad. For just a split second you can lose your footing on the stairs and fall down them - this has happened to me in the past. Imagine having a blackout, no matter how brief, whilst boiling a kettle of water or crossing the road! It doesn't take long to turn an everyday activity into a disaster. On several occasions I have poured boiling water onto my hand instead of into a cup, and stuck my hands into the flames of a gas hob. These have not resulted in major injuries, but they were extremely unpleasant nonetheless.

Another difficulty is that any seizure, no matter how small, can leave the sufferer feeling weakened and confused. The more absences I have the worse this becomes, and some quite small seizures can leave me feeling as bad as if I had had a major fit.

Does the electricity in thunderstorms affect you?

Well, I have to say I have never had a problem with this. During a storm, I simply enjoy the wonders of nature, watching the lightning and listening to the rolls of thunder. The only time I have had a problem with storms is when a sudden clap of thunder makes me jump, and this can easily trigger off a seizure.

Why does your family often have to check up on you? If you are having a seizure, surely they would hear it. Aren't they being a little over protective?

Once again, we are back to the myth that all seizures are big ones. People who know me well can tell a great deal from the occasional silences, for instance. They may be talking to me but I don't respond. I could be holding a cup of coffee and they know straight away what that silence means, so they take the hot cup out of my hands. If I accidentally drop a saucepan or knock into a table, I will shout out: "I'm all right" because the first thought when people hear such a noise is one of concern, they always fear the worst. My family have often said that they live on a knife edge with me, never knowing from one moment to the next whether I'm going to be safe. By listening out for the silence of a small seizure, they have frequently saved me from falling down stairs, or scalding myself.

Is it difficult living with epilepsy? Do you often lose heart?

I try to accept my situation and not fight it. It is difficult living with epilepsy but I take every day as it comes and enjoy each moment of the good days. From time to time, I do lose heart and get depressed as anyone would, but the important thing is to bounce back and in this way the lows do not last for long.

You are not in a wheelchair, why do you view yourself as being disabled?

Because epilepsy is not obvious unless a seizure is occurring, people often think there is not a problem. Well, how about trying to cross a road, or walk down stairs blind-folded. Epilepsy is worse than that. Your brain cuts out for anything from a split second to several minutes, and you don't know anything about it. Although I am the same as anyone else for most of the time, I am frequently severely disabled for short periods. In fact, I may well be at greater risk of injury or even death than someone who is permanently in a wheelchair.

Do you have a faith? If so, does it help you?

I never have been a religious person. I don't believe in God. I think my convent education and the frequent religious lessons put me off the idea. I do believe in leading a good and honest life, and enjoying it as far as possible. I find this keeps me going through thick and thin. My faith is my life, not what might come afterwards.

Do you find it difficult to understand or learn new things?

This question always makes me angry. I am not an idiot. Sometimes I may have blank spots and falls during my day, but this does not make me 'slow'. Epilepsy is not a mental condition but a physical one, a neurological one to be precise. It is true that some people who have epilepsy may also have conditions such as autism, but this is like saying someone with flu may also have a heart attack. The two are completely separate conditions and have no bearing on each other. What I do have is a problem with my memory. I will often have to be taught something a few times before it really sinks in, because I will have forgotten some of what I was told originally. This is common in people with epilepsy.

Didn't you feel bitter when your weight went over 20 stone as a result of your medication?

I realised I was big, but just presumed it was because I had always been large, plus the fact that I was pregnant at the time. It never occurred to me that my weight could been worsened by the anti-convulsants. My weight plummeted to a mere eleven stone when my medication was changed. I really looked anorexic, considering I am six foot tall. However, my weight eventually stabilised and now I try hard to keep to my recommended size so I never become enormous again. The episode did not leave me bitter because I accepted it as just one of the side effects of the medication I was on.

How do foods affect your condition?

Epilepsy is not like a migraine where you can say foods such as cheese will affect you. Food is definitely not an issue in my case.

Having said that, children with severe epilepsy up to the onset of adolescence can sometimes be helped by the Ketogenic Diet which is high in fat and low in carbohydrate and protein. It appears to be useful for various different types of seizure, such as myoclonic jerks, minor motor seizures, tonic-clonic and complex partial seizures. For some reason this diet is not effective in adults though the reasons are not clear

Did you often ask the teacher at school to repeat things because of absences?

I didn't bother because it would mean stopping the class every few minutes. So I just sailed on the breeze and hoped that I got what the teacher had said. Sometimes I did and other times I did not. If I was worried that I had missed something, I would ask my best friend after the lesson and she would fill me in. In the end I would take it as 'normal' that I would miss some of the words or a couple of sentences, and I coped anyway.

What is the first thing you do or think of when you recover from a tonic-clonic seizure?

The first thing I say to myself is: "oh no not again". I always know when one has taken place, I am not sure how, but I do. Perhaps it is the strange taste that I sometimes experience afterwards. Then I will usually try to get back on my feet again, though this is often a struggle. I might also apologise to bystanders. Just recently a seizure occurred and once I had managed to get over the stress and strains of it, I found that I had cleaned up the house. I don't recall doing it. In fact, I remember nothing that happened for well over an hour after the seizure.

Have you found epilepsy restricting throughout your life?

Epilepsy is as restricting as you let it be. It inevitably has some effect on my home and working life. For instance, I often need someone to be with me when I am doing something like shopping. I always have to be careful about day to day living, not getting over-excited or worked up about things. I am not permitted to drive a car, and even bus travel can be dangerous, so I have to use taxis when I travel on my own.

The solution is to concentrate on enjoying the things that are possible and there are many of those - not those that should not be done. I try to adopt a calm attitude, which for me is not as easy as it may sound. Since my childhood I have always tried to keep my everyday life happy and contented, and to make sure that a smile is always there.

16

Who cares?

W ho cares that at some moment in time I could have a seizure? Members of the public? Yes, to a certain extent they do. The ones that do not panic can do the right thing. However, closer to home there are the ones that care every hour of every day, 365 days a year. These are the people who are closest, family, friends and work colleagues who spend the most time with me.

In a series of informal interviews, they told me in which way they would routinely monitor whether I was all right. I spoke to my sons, Paul and David, my husband, a friend and several of my colleagues at the Oxfam shop and the disability centre where I work as a volunteer.

Almost everybody commented that they listen out for strange noises and, interestingly, any lack of noise that would indicate that I was having a seizure. David listens out for my splashing in the bath, and he even counts the stairs when I am coming down them. He also notices my speech slowing down, or perhaps panting, prior to a seizure. If I am washing up, Paul will listen for the moment when the noise of the pots and pans is replaced by silence, and call out "are you OK, Mum?" He is also alert to any crashes that would indicate a fall or loss of consciousness. For that reason. I make a point of shouting that I am OK if I accidentally drop something. This listening habit is something picked up quite quickly by family, friends and colleagues.

Most people also reported keeping an eye on me for such things as movements in my hands and suddenly standing still. They tended to do this out of the corner of the eye, rather than staring. It seems that everybody is tuned in, waiting, but without being overly worried.

They were also very aware of the need for me to stay safe, and would from time to time remind me that I was doing something potentially dangerous. Such bad habits include sitting on the edge of a chair, cradling a hot cup of coffee in my hands, and using a kitchen knife to peel potatoes. These are things that most people take for granted but can be dangerous for me. My husband will also try to keep me calm, because if I get in too much of a state I am inclined to have nasty seizures. When I asked a friend about staying safe, she mentioned that within the past few minutes she had just reminded me to sit back on the chair. We both laughed as she said she was always doing this.

David said he had to keep an eye on me for most of the day and had learnt to do this from when he was a very small child, as had Paul. It had become part of their way of life, something that went with Mum. Over the years, my husband has become a very light sleeper which may be because at one stage I was having seizures during my sleep as well as when I was awake, and he would have to wake suddenly to make sure I was safe. The last seizure happened during my sleep about two or three years ago, but still he remains a light sleeper.

Anyone trying to understand epilepsy could take note of the Police song: "Every breathe you take, every move you make, every step you take, I'll be watching you." It seems in all cases everybody is tuned in, waiting, without being overly worried.

I also asked those people how they felt about having to take some responsibility for my personal safety.

David replied that his stomach turns when he realises I am going to fall, but he is mainly concerned in case I hurt myself. Apart from that he just gets on with doing what is necessary to help me and to ease the situation. He does not find it easy to cope with serious seizures, but he takes every day as it comes and regards it as a challenge to get me through each day safely, without damage or injury. I asked him whether he finds it tiring or depressing. He said he did not, despite having seen many horrific things that have happened to me over the years. David has had to cope with my epilepsy from when he was very young and it has become second nature to help where he can.

Paul said that seeing me constantly unwell is very tiring and sometimes even depressing, adding that it is often very hard work. He too wouldn't think twice about helping me, though. "It is part of you", he said.

My husband finds my seizures very tiring and stressful. Like me, he is always hoping that one day my epilepsy will be properly controlled. As with my sons, he regards the condition as part of me and can accept it without question. He finds it hard work dealing with epilepsy on a regular basis. In particular, the regular hospital trips to London are very stressful because he must stay by my side on crowded tubes and trains in case I have a seizure that he has to deal with. He does it without question because he cares.

A good friend agreed with others that after all the time she has known me the seizures have become a way of life and part of what makes 'me'. She added that epilepsy is part of life and shouldn't be dwelt upon. Instead it was important to move on and get on with the rest of life.

At 85, Vi was one of the oldest ladies at the Oxfam shop. Unlike many of the older people I have referred to in this book, she took my seizures in her stride. She was one in a million! I have had many seizures in the shop and she apparently always felt helpless. She felt there was nothing she could do to prevent the seizure from happening. All she could do is stand by and watch, and take basic first aid steps which she came to know very well. She has dealt with seizures, both large and small, and despite her age has always managed to cope with the situation.

The manageress of the shop said that she didn't leave me on my own for long periods on the till. Every now and again she would look from the back room to make sure all was well. She regarded checking on me as just another chore in the shop's day. When a seizure occurred, she would get cross, not because I was causing trouble in the shop, but because it just didn't seem fair that I had to go through it on a regular basis. She says she manages my condition by treating me the same as any other person, and takes any problems as they come. The staff have got to know me well over the years and I am now an accepted member of the team.

Those who work alongside me at the disability centre check on me once in a while but felt that I would normally do all that was required of me anyway. One of the things they check for is that the chair I use does not have wheels. Usually we have a shuffle of chairs when I arrive to make sure I am safely seated. They agreed that epilepsy had now become a fairly regular thing for them and the best way for them is not to worry about it. When asked if they found my condition tiring or depressing, their response was: "Don't be daft!"

These are just some of the people that care in their own unique and special ways. There are many more out there. I would like to dedicate this chapter to them, for all the help, love and patience they have shown me, and others like me over many years. I am sure I am not just one of the lucky ones. There are many more. To carer's everywhere, I say a very warm "thank you."

Weathering the Storms - living with epilepsy

17

A week from the diary

When I was thirty-two and my sons were aged three and five, I started writing a diary. In those days, my seizures where more severe than they are now, with the major (grand mal) ones happening daily. I have selected some diary entries to give an idea of what it was like for a typical week of my life.

22/9/87

My back is still aching from the seizure I threw the other day, but I was determined to get my washing dry. The only sound I could hear was the noise of lawnmowers, everyone getting their last cut in before autumn raised its ugly head. Except for me that is. The lawnmower is another thing I am forbidden to touch - just in case I have a blackout and put my fingers into the rotating blades. I sighed deeply to myself, promptly followed by a childish giggle. At least I can't be blamed if the grass gets too long, I thought!

Then I suddenly felt strange. The only way to describe it is that I didn't feel united with my body. Every breath I tried to draw seemed unable to enter me - a very weird sensation. Then the world seemed to fade away completely and that was the last thing I can remember. The morning became an entire blank. I vaguely remember coming to, choking, unable to breath. Thank goodness for my home-help. She stood beside me hitting me across the back to try to get me to vomit. She knew this would help me breath properly. I remember bits of that frightful day - not a lot but some. I remember my home-help standing there with not a trace of panic on her face, just the warmth and kindness and above all the understanding that was always there. I became rather bitter at this point. "Why me?" I said to her. "Some people don't live their lives to the full - they don't enjoy the things that stare them in the face every day of their lives. I do, so why me?" She smiled at me trying to comfort me as best she could. Later, I could have bitten my tongue, and thought it had been a wicked thing to say. People live their lives the way they want, not the way I want them to.

The rest of the morning is a complete blank. Apparently I went to the local shops about a hundred yards away, but I don't remember it. I've discovered in the years of having epilepsy that the after-effects can be just as bad, or at least as nearly as bad, as the seizure itself.

You never feel the attack , but when you recover consciousness, a vile taste sometimes appears. The confusion you experience is like 'the morning after the night before', only you don't get the enjoyment of the drink first! Every bone and every muscle says to you: "we're not going to move for you, we've just done a whole load of shaking. What do you think we are, slaves or something?" My eyes look heavy or swollen, my speech is slow or even slurred and these effects can last for several hours. I've got several hours to go yet as I had a second seizure about an hour ago . . . .

23/9/87

Another beautiful September day shows its face through the gap in the curtain, yesterday seems a million miles away. The terrible experience I had of choking my life away is now past. Another day has started and out there is my future, more new experiences just waiting for me. I sat on the side of the bed listening to the children with their giggling and arguing that always seems to occur at this time of the morning.

Once again, I could feel that strange feeling of not being able to breath - another seizure coming. "Damn you!", I remember thinking to myself, "I want to enjoy this warm and beautiful day". The seizure lasted only a matter of minutes. Afterwards, I wasn't so confused as I was yesterday and I could tell what had happened by that strange taste in my mouth. At least today I was able to get my body to move - not that it really wanted to, but it recognised who was in charge - me!

I looked at my husband, who was still sleeping peacefully. "What a life he and the kids must have" I thought, "How on earth do they cope?" Somehow they accept my epilepsy as part of our lifestyle, with never a grumble or complaint. I wouldn't swap any of them for all the health, riches and finery in the world - and that is a promise. "Mike", I called in a soft voice, he replied with a groan. I called again, this time I got a "morning" as a reply. The next stage was to get him aware of the situation. I said "I've just had one of those partial seizures, can you help?" Like the seventh cavalry, he moved quickly. The covers were thrown off the bed, and once more he moved into action. Much of the time there is not a lot he can do - apart from being there and waiting together to see if a big seizure will follow. It gives me the support that is needed to get over it on a day to day basis.

25/9/87

Today was a difficult one. Last night I had a chat with my son's teacher about bullying, and this worried me so much that I had a rather a violent seizure in the local supermarket this morning. Whilst unconscious, I tried to carry on with what I was doing. It was obvious that the owner, Jim, did not know what to do. He tried to force me into sitting down, I resisted and he received a left hander on the shoulder. Like me, he has a sense of humour thank goodness, and could see the funny side of the situation. In fact when I did apologise, he burst out laughing. Even his eyes were smiling at me: "Don't worry it's part of life and I accept the good days with the bad days" he said. "If only everyone thought in this way" I said to myself.

26/9/87

It is a bright and sunny Saturday, if a little cool. Six year old Paul has gone into the town with a twelve year old girl. She has become part of the family. We've known her several years now, and sometimes I look on her like my own daughter. She has seen me have many disastrous seizures but I have never yet seen her upset by one. Not a bad reference to give someone so young.

Paul was telling me this morning, that it won't be long until harvest festival at his school. He is very proud. He has been asked to read a lesson to the rest of the school and all of the parents. He said: "don't worry Mum, I know you probably won't come to see me at the festival because of your seizures, but it really doesn't matter." I could feel the churning inside me. I am a normal person after all, it is just that sometimes, my brain goes haywire. If only some kind of warning took place, life would be so much easier. "It doesn't though, Julie", I thought, "so stop feeling so sorry for yourself. You've got arms and legs, a wonderful husband, two 'normal' little boys - that's a lot more than most." Somehow, I would get to that harvest festival by hook or by crook, with or without a 'minder', in order to hear Paul's reading. I told him my intentions and he beamed with pride.

30/9/87

The children insisted on waking me up at 5.15am saying "mum we want our breakfast, we're hungry". This is perhaps why I collapsed outside the house this morning on the way to our local shops. Luckily, I was chatting to a neighbour and she realised what was happening and managed to drag me back into the house. I am no light weight, and she was rather an elderly lady, so I don't know how she did it. Rather stupidly, about two hours later I decided to carry on with my trip to the shops. I did my shopping but I don't remember anything about it. The people in the local shops know me very well so they knew roughly what I wanted as I wouldn't have much of an idea myself.

I find it best, in cases such as these, to count my blessings. I fell into a flower bed and my head is still rather bruised and battered - but it could have been a lot worse. My head might have been damaged if I had fallen onto the concrete pavement.

It's a good job my home help was here to help me as Paul chose today to have a tummy ache and not go to school. He insisted on playing his videos too loud, and needed reminding that I was trying to recover.

Here I sit, with my feet up on a stool, not knowing how long I will be able to keep my eyes open. I find writing this is becoming more and more difficult, but my pride and determination will not let me stop. It is something I know I am going to do. I can definitely say that it has been 'one of those days'.

1/10/87

David has finally arrived home from playschool. His mind is so active, and his physical energy is second to none. Sometimes I wish I had his energy. He is rather a handful. He has had to learn in his four years of life that mum, from time to time, collapses or blacks out. Fortunately, children accept things far easier than adults. I have noticed that the children in our neighbourhood don't seem to worry about my seizures. My epilepsy does not frighten them. They seem to look on it as they would any other illness or condition.

Some time ago, there was a couple who would not allow their children near ours. The woman did not talk to me, either. My friends and family said that was her loss. I made a point of not being bitter about it. I had always assumed that the couple were like that because of my illness, and I did eventually find out that this was the case. Family and friends had always sowed the seeds of doubt so I could always cling onto the idea that maybe I had upset her in some way. They thought that this would hurt me less than knowing the truth, but the one thing they forgot to take into consideration was peace of mind and for me this was important. I was not upset. Instead I felt sorry for the couple. If anything, I think I felt a little angry as my boys were only young and had to suffer as well.

2/10/87

Before my home-help left to go to her next client, she made me a cup of coffee. This was because I cannot make myself a hot drink unless someone else is with me. Otherwise it can be a dangerous thing to do. Like many disabled people I find this sort of restriction really annoying, because I would like to be an active person. I get very annoyed with myself sometimes, or perhaps I should say with my condition. The restrictions, at times, quite seem endless.

For instance, I cannot take the boys round the block on their bikes as the risk of me falling onto concrete is too high. I have never taken my children to school. Instead, they attend in a taxi. Unfortunately I cannot take responsibility for their safety as they will be looking out for mine. Sometimes, I peer through the net curtains watching other mums going to collect their children from school, and envy them.

As a child, I can remember thinking what it would be like to have babies, and then taking them to school with the other mums. I wanted to join the PTA and help with school bazaars and jumble sales. My own mother always took part in school events, and was extremely supportive towards the school. I was very proud of my mum for doing this. So many parents didn't even take an interest and I vowed never to be one of those people. If only I had foreseen the future at that age.

In the past, sport played a large part in my life, but now I must play the part of a spectator. When I watch swimming on television, I can't help looking back to the days when I was able to take part in competitions and races. When I was 12, I was junior swimming champion for our area. As my husband says, it's no good looking back. Looking forward is what counts. It is nice, though, to savour those moments, as memories can't be taken away.

8/10/87

Dear Diary, I'm sorry I didn't get down to writing to you before. I feel that if I had written yesterday my annoyance, anger and general upset would have produced an entry that was too bitter. I had to have a little time to get it out of my system.

Let me explain. Yesterday was Harvest Festival day, Paul's big day for reading in public. I promised I would be there, and I was. My carer and I put on our finery and went to the school. The hall was packed, row after row, with mums all sitting and chatting to each other before the service started. My son's headmistress was standing in the doorway. She saw me and said: "Ah, Mrs Dennison, here you are. I have reserved two seats for you and your friend". The chairs were on their own at the back of the hall, away from all the other mums and the rest of the audience. I felt like a leper, dirty, unclean, and above all belittled. She walked off which was probably for the best, or I think I may have said something that I would have regretted later.

My carer turned to me. She could see the anger and hurt written all over my face. Gently, she clutched my hand, but didn't say anything, she didn't have to. She knew every emotion I was feeling. A friend of mine who was sitting in the 'proper seats' in front of us saw me, and could see what was going through my mind. Without speaking she picked up her chair, as if in protest, banged it down next to mine and then said "Hi Julie, how are you doing mate". She, too, could see the upset on my face. I decided that I would not be treated in a way that was different to anybody else. I left my chair and stood alongside the other mums. My friend and my carer did the same. I wanted my son to feel proud because I was there watching him and encouraging him when he had his lesson to read. He was proud of me. And I was so, so proud of him when he stood up to read from the Bible.

18 Medicine, side-effects and alternatives

A ccording to Jean Barclay's *A Caring Community: a centenary history of the NSE and Chalfont Centre 1892 - 1992*, the use of medicine for epilepsy is a fairly modern concept. Before the mid 19th century, epilepsy was treated with metallic salts, setons (applying silk or cotton threads under the skin), blisters and cupping. Later, bromide salts were used, especially potassium bromide. They were a break-through for larger seizures.

Until this time, the public believed that people with epilepsy were possessed by the devil. By 1873, much research work was done on partial seizures by Hughlings Jackson. He concluded that seizures were: "excessive and disorderly discharge of nerve tissues on mus-cles." This research work finally started to banish the idea of demon-ising. It was also realised that epilepsy is not necessarily "the falling sickness".

Although towards the end of the 19th century, there was some understanding of the different types of seizure and their origin, there remained many unknowns about the timing and causes of epilepsy.

In Victorian times, epilepsy had its problems socially. There were many jobs forbidden to sufferers. Women with epilepsy could not work in factories, as servants, or shop assistants. Many earned little more than a pittance doing sweated work at home. Men, too, had their difficulties,. They were not allowed to use machinery, climb lad-ders or work near furnaces. More and more epilepsy sufferers were having to go to work-houses - very grim places indeed.

Fortunately, the 20th century has seen major developments in epilepsy control. Many drugs have been produced for epilepsy over the past hundred years. There are at least fifteen other drugs in com-mon usage. Phenobarbitone was first introduced in 1912, whereas Topiramate was only introduced in 1995. A great deal of research is still being carried out in the field of epilepsy and new medications are becoming available all the time. Since the 1990s, there has been a new drug available every couple of years.

Because of this, the majority of people with epilepsy can easily be treated. Usually once the correct medication is prescribed, the chances of having seizures is greatly reduced, provided of course that the pills are taken regularly. Three-quarters have no seizures on medication. Their lives are nowhere near as bad as they had feared when epilepsy was first diagnosed.

Another improvement over the last century is that members of the public have much less negative attitudes towards epilepsy and those that suffer from it. This has been helped by a considerable increase in the amount of knowledge available to the general public. If people don't know anything about epilepsy, or about anything else for that matter, they are bound to misunderstand it.

Most sufferers carry on normal everyday lives and can enjoy their days to the full provided they are wary when in potentially dangerous situations. A small percentage are not properly controlled by drugs. Although I consider myself as one of these, I have seen many people worse off than me during my numerous stays in hospital. Some have to wear crash helmets all of the time because their seizures are so regular that there is a high risk of head injury. Because epilepsy is a symptom of many serious brain disorders, the worst epilepsy sufferers may have other problems, and some have to spend their time in wheelchairs. So every time I get a little depressed, I think about these people: I have a far greater chance than they do of my condition being cured or controlled.

Over the past forty years. I have been prescribed most of the epilepsy medicines on the market. However, none has been totally successful and often the benefit is very short-lived. This is unusual as most people's epilepsy is controlled fairly easily. I am one of only twenty per cent who are not particularly responsive to the medication.

As a child I used Phenobarbitone and continued with it right up to my teenage years. It kept my bigger seizures to a minimum for quite some while, but eventually I had to change to other drugs such as Phenytoin and Clobazam. By the time I was twenty I was on another well known drug, Epilim. Each of these medicines did the trick for a while, but none gave me really long term control.

In recent years, I have participated in trials of new drugs. These are ones that do not yet have a general licence in this country. I had to sign a declaration to show that I was willing to take part in the trial. Unfortunately, none of them helped. However, as I have always said, you don't know until you try.

Any drug has the possibility of side effects and anti-epileptic medication is included in this. The side effects fall into three main groups. Allergic reaction, which is rare, usually takes the form of a skin rash and medical advice should be sought. Far more common are dose-related effects such as drowsiness or unsteadiness, or even lack of concentration or poor memory. Lastly, and these are also rare, are long term (chronic) effects that result from the person using the drug over a long period.

Many people may never suffer from these side-effects, but as you will have gathered already I am usually the exception! I have found that one of the most common effects are dizziness, weakness or even tiredness, but have experienced some quite nasty effects, including sore and painful rashes, tremors, swelling of the gums, nausea and irritability, lack of appetite, and considerable weight gain.

One of the drugs was quite effective, but in order to keep it working I needed to be prescribed more and more until my quality of life was affected in two ways. Firstly, the increasing doses made me more zombie-like each day. My actions and movements were all much slower and my speech was slurred. As a result I could do very little. Secondly, whilst taking this medicine I put on several stones in weight and became quite obese. As soon as I was changed to another drug, the effect was dramatic. In a matter of months, I went from twenty two stone to about eleven, and was the smallest size I have ever been. Surprisingly, this was not good news. I looked positively skeletal. Shortly afterwards we moved to a different county and on a visit to the local hospital my husband and I were split up and interviewed separately because they thought I had anorexia nervosa. It took a while to explain that it was probably the effect of the anti-convulsants, not the fact that I didn't eat.

Another drug seemed helpful to begin with, then the problems started. The first few weeks of taking it were marvellous. I hardly had a seizure at all and it gave me a new lease of life. I was so pleased that I telephoned the hospital to tell the doctors. But after a few weeks, I started to lose a lot of weight. For some reason I did not feel like eating. I would eat half a helping of everything, then leave the rest of it on my plate. This did not worry me. I had always been on the heavy side, so to lose a bit of weight did not seem to be a problem. However, the weight loss started to creep up and my weight went from fifteen and a half stone to about twelve. The pounds were coming off on a weekly basis but nobody knew whether it was the medication or not. As a precaution, I was taken off the tablet and the weight loss stopped. Although this could eventually have been dangerous, these weeks of slimming turned out to have been a bonus. I had reached a weight I was happy with and I have worked hard ever since to make sure I kept at that size.

Some pills I had as a child made me feel tired, but I have always been renowned for my pig-headedness, so I never let the fact that I was tired stop me doing things. Somehow I would gather energy and carry on.

I have always slept very heavily. Perhaps this was because I was always tired, or maybe I am just a heavy sleeper. I also snore very badly. Nothing can waken me, not even thunder storms or high winds. This is obviously annoying for my partner who can shake me over and over again but still I will not wake. A sleep test was done in hospital, just to see if any results of it would help, but unfortunately they did not. I don't know whether this is connected with my epilepsy, the medication, or if it is just me.

When I was pregnant all medication was reduced substantially, because of the effect it might have on my unborn children. Despite this, both of my children were quite shaky when they were new-born and I was told that they were experiencing withdrawal symptoms from the anti-convulsants in my (and therefore their) bloodstream. This lasted only a few days, however.

My experience, though this is fortunately rare, is of tablets that do not control the problem or those that have unacceptable side-effects. I have been told I have tried just about everything - I have even participated in trials of drugs that never reached the market - but nothing seems to work. At least so far.

Anti epileptic medication can react to other medications taken, so care is needed. Also it is essential to use a good pharmacist who can advise you. The contraceptive pill may become less effective, so

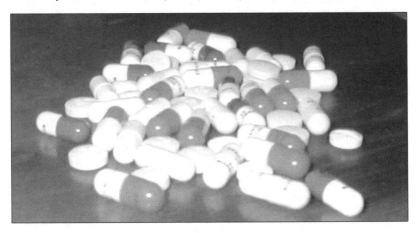

The pills I take in a week just to get a small amount of 'control'

Weathering the Storms - living with epilepsy

women using anti epileptic medication may need a higher dose contraceptive.

Alcohol can sometimes react with medication, and some people say it is best not to drink alcohol at all if you are on anti-convulsants. My own experience is that moderate use of alcohol - I make one drink last all evening - has little effect. Drugs such as amphetamines, cocaine, heroin and ecstasy are known to cause an increase in the frequency of seizures. Moderate use of cannabis may not be harmful, though there is likely to be an increase of seizures in the withdrawal of the substance.

Different medication can have different side effects, so changing to another tablet, or even just reducing the dose, will usually stop these side effects happening. That is why it is important to keep regular appointments with the doctor. Everything may feel fine but it is always best to check that the dose is not too high.

Although conventional anti-convulsant drugs are the main way to treat epilepsy, there are alternatives. This includes stimulation of a nerve, brain surgery, a special diet, and so-called alternative medicine such as acupuncture and aroma therapy.

People with epilepsy that does not respond to drug treatment may benefit from having a vagal nerve stimulator inserted into their neck. As its name implies, the stimulator applies a mild electrical signal to the vagus nerve which is one of many that carry signals to and from the brain. This can reduce the seizure frequency in some people. Epilepsy is caused by little electrical storms in the head, and the stimulator may be able to stop this abnormal brain activity. A small generator similar to a pace-maker is attached to the vagus nerve in a one to two hour operation. The doctor then programmes the generator with different frequencies of stimulation to suit the individual. This treatment is still very new so long term guides to side effects have not been established yet. However, people who have been fitted with one have sometimes complained of tingling in the neck when the nerve is being stimulated, or they have experienced hoarseness. I do not have first hand experience of this treatment yet, and it is too new to judge how effective it is. It is, however, an option for those of us that have tried everything else.

What about brain surgery? Well, of the twenty per cent of epilepsy sufferers who fail to respond to other treatments, only three per cent can be put forward for surgery. Of those who are operated upon, about 70% become totally seizure free. So for a few, it can effect a cure. Why so few? Several things have to be considered before surgery can be done. Anti-epileptic medication must have been tried but found unsuccessful. Seizures should be found to be coming from one localised area of the brain. The person should have no other medical problem that would make them unsuitable for surgery. Their ability to carry on normally after surgery would not be affected by removing that particular part of the brain. No other part of the brain would be affected by the surgery. The areas involving speech, sight, movement and hearing are not close to the piece of brain to be removed. And most importantly, the person must be thought to have a very good chance of becoming seizure free after the operation. Extensive tests are done to assess if the person is suitable for surgery. This is a possibility for me for the future.

There is little scientific evidence regarding 'alternative therapies'. They should not be used to replace conventional drugs, but more as an aid to anti-epileptic medication. They can be helpful in giving people with epilepsy a feeling of control over their bodies and their lives, and in general improve their sense of well being. Also, many people, including myself, find they have more seizures during times of stress, so anything that reduces stress could lead to greater seizure control.

Aromatherapy uses aromatic oils taken from plants to reduce stress. The oils are diluted and rubbed into the skin and then work on the brain. Several oils, Jasmine, Ylang Ylang, Camomile, and Lavender, may be helpful in cases of epilepsy as they all have a calming effect. However, some oils, such as Rosemary, Fennel and Sage should be avoided

I tried acupuncture for a while but did not find it effective. This is a very old treatment that uses needles which are inserted into the flesh for a period ranging from a few seconds to thirty minutes. In a 1999 Norwegian study, 29 epilepsy sufferers were treated with acupuncture. The group was split into two; fifteen had acupuncture and the remaining fourteen had a sham acupuncture. This was to see whether acupuncture was indeed a viable help to the condition. There was seizure reduction in both groups, but it did not reach a statistical significance. The test was unable to prove a beneficial effect in epilepsy. Acupuncture may, however, be effective in reducing stress and anxiety, which may be helpful for epilepsy sufferers.

Biofeedback is a type of behavioural therapy which can be helpful to people with certain types of seizure. It involves learning mental techniques to regulate the electrical activity in the brain, over a period of time, In this way it is possible to prevent seizures from spreading. This method has been known to increase the patient's self-esteem because it gives a sense of control over their epilepsy. It requires a lot of dedication from the therapist and much concentration and motivation from the patient. It is usually only used on people over the age of 14.

Homeopathy is sometimes used alongside drug treatment . It is a branch of medicine which sees symptoms as the body's reaction to illness, and tries to overcome it. A practitioner would use small doses of substances to stimulate the body and restore health.

Herbal medicine is not generally used to treat epilepsy. The plant extracts used have a combination of active constituents which restore the natural balance of the body and encourage healing. People taking anti-epileptic drugs shouldn't take herbal medicine for another condition without first seeing the doctor or herbal practitioner.

Does food affect epilepsy? For most people with epilepsy, as with the population as a whole, a good, healthy, balanced diet is best. Food allergies might affect seizures in some people, but there is very little evidence to support this. Some children with very severe epilepsy may be helped by the Ketogenic diet. This is a high fat, low protein regime which can be quite unpalatable and therefore difficult to keep up. It should only be used in consultation with a doctor and dietician. Unfortunately its success is only limited and it is not effective in adults.

Reflexology can be relaxing and also reduce stress. The treatment involves foot massage that initiates healing in the body.

Other alternative therapies are Autogenic therapy, Tai Chi, and also Yoga. These too, can be relaxing and lower stress.

Any alternative therapies should always be discussed with your doctor before using them, especially if you are tempted to stop taking your normal medicine.

19 The ins and outs of being a patient

There are two very different types of hospital patient. One is the out-patient who visits the specialist every so often to check that the medication is still working, and to discuss new developments. The other is the in-patient, resident in the hospital for a period so that tests or an operation can be carried out. I have been both of these on many occasions throughout my life.

I find that being an out patient is just as stressful as spending time on a hospital ward. I attend the National Hospital for Neurology every five or six weeks, and have done for some twenty-five years.

I live quite close to the hospital. The journey, which uses car, train, tube and foot takes just one hour from door to door. Some patients travel hundreds of miles just to see the specialist. Although the trains are frequent, I hate the journey. The carriages are crowded and smelly. The tube train which goes below central London involves a lot of hustle and bustle, pushing and shoving. The hospital is like a second home, but during the journey I become more nervous as I sit watching the world pass by.

For safety reasons, I can't travel alone, so a helper, usually my husband comes with me. Fortunately, not only are my rail fares reduced - one of the few perks of being disabled - but the person who has to look after me also has a cheaper ticket.

I have always been a regular out-patient, but when I was a child I went to the local hospital. I remember that I would take a half day off school on a Friday which meant missing hockey, which was a lesson I enjoyed. My mother would pick me up from school so I would see the doctor in my smart school uniform, topped off with a straw boater. I saw the doctor only once every few months, as my condition was not so serious then, but I remember it being a stressful experience.

During the first few years of going to the National Hospital, the wait to see the doctor would last a minimum of two hours, and often it would be six. What was worse, no-one could tell me how long I had to wait, so there was no chance of getting some fresh air or having lunch out. This was plainly unacceptable, and it was addressed when the National Health Service was shaken up in the 1980s. Now, the waiting time can be as little as a few minutes, but is sometimes still an hour or more, depending on the doctor's caseload.

A typical visit might go like this:

The waiting room is crowded with patients from different cultures and backgrounds. On seeing this I think that the wait will be hours. The fact that all of the patients have some kind of neurological problem gives a feeling of camaraderie as we all have something in common.

We queue up at the reception desk to book me in. The queue contains a mass of people, some of them who have travelled hundreds of miles to see the doctor. Some have waited two or three months for their appointment to come around again whilst others have waited a year because their problem is not as serious as others.

The Women's Royal Voluntary Service (WRVS) run a coffee shop in the waiting room. So before taking my seat we get in provisions for the wait, usually cans of fizzy drink and chocolate biscuits.

During the wait - in summer a very hot and sticky experience - my anxiety builds up gradually as I try to remember all of the things I want to tell the doctor. This is not an easy task. I am almost certain that I will come away from the hospital without remembering something that could be important to my case. I mumble underneath my breath that I should write it down on paper next time - but I never do. Then my name is called, but only to ask me to sit in a corridor outside the consulting rooms. This is progress of sorts as I know the wait is almost at an end.

Whilst waiting, I watch the nursing and administrative staff rushing around. They all manage to smile and have that warm glow that portrays caring and kindness. On occasion, they take abuse from patients who are tired of waiting, but they keep smiling. The hospital staff have always treated me with respect and that means a lot to me. I have been going there for so long that many of them greet me like an old friend.

The previous patient comes out and at last it is my turn. The doctor gives me a big smile as he greets me and asks me into his surgery. I have often wondered how he stays cheerful when he has to deal with people's problems all day. We shake hands and sit down. "How have you been", is always the first question. I detail my seizures, large and small, and any other strange symptoms that may or may not be side effects of the medication. The doctor adds these to the two large volumes that make up my hos-

The National Hospital for Neurology and Neurosurgery in Queen Square, London, where I regularly see some of the world's top epilepsy specialists. The tall building on the left is the Institute of Neurology

pital notes. It's surprising how much can be written about 25 years of my life.

Next we discuss whether the current medication is producing enough control over the epilepsy. My usual answer is "no!" Sometimes a blood test is called for to see if the level of medication in my body is too high, or too low?

Then the topic almost certainly moves to new developments in epilepsy control. I have had all of the drugs on the market, so my only hope is some new wonder pill, or some other method of treatment. The doctor does his best to assure me that eventually something will be found that will control my seizures. This prevents me getting too despondent, which I must admit I do from time to time, if things get very bad. He listens to all the comments I have to say and explains what the next step will be, and how long it may take.

After my allotted 20-30 minutes, the appointment is over and we leave. I breathe a sigh of relief because I always find the experience stressful, feeling that I should have said more or remembered something vital. Nevertheless, these regular sessions are like a lifeline. They serve to reassure me that there is ultimately some hope of a better life. So when the doctor says to me: "I will see you in a few weeks' time", it seems like an age.

From time to time my seizures get so bad that I have to spend days, or even weeks, in hospital as an in-patient. This can be a gruelling experience, or it can be quite fun, depending upon why I am there and which hospital I am in, because each has its own characteristics.

The National Society for Epilepsy has a specialist hospital at Chalfont in Buckinghamshire, and every few years I spend several weeks in their Assessment Unit. This is totally different from any hospital I have been in. The lovely grounds extend over several acres, and when my husband visits we enjoy walking around the site. In the grounds there are bungalows housing people who are chronically ill with epilepsy, so that they can live in a safe environment.

The Assessment Unit is for those of us with serious problems, but who can live in the community. People like me - or even those who are more seriously disabled - come here to undergo investigations and be carefully watched over a long period to see when and if seizures occur.

Although the accommodation in the Assessment Unit is similar to a hospital ward, little time is spent in bed. All of the patients have some kind of epilepsy, with different degrees of severity. When I was there, there were about 30 of us and we talked endlessly with one another whilst sitting in the 'smoking room', which was actually an old conservatory. Even those who did not smoke would sit there for the company, or walk around the lovely grounds of the hospital. The patients are encouraged to live as near normal life as possible. We made our own beds. Other chores, such as laying up the table for meals are done according to a rota.

As the patients' seizures are monitored continuously, it is necessary to have a large number of nursing staff. The staff to patient ratio is about 1:2, much higher than in a general hospital., and each patient has a case worker allotted to them The nurses seemed to be more like friends than staff, and patients are encouraged to call them by

Weathering the Storms - living with epilepsy

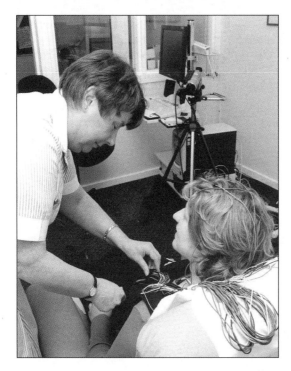

An electroencephalo-gram picks up minute electrical signals in the brain. It is some-times accompanied by a timed video recording.
[Photograph: National Society for Epilepsy]

their first names. Everything is done to make the stay as pleasant as possible.

During the long stay, I started to feel at home and I made many friends. The one thing I had in common with the other patients was my epilepsy. We all suffered and we suffered together. We became a large family.

I underwent many types of tests including an Electroencephalo-gram (conveniently abbreviated to EEG) and a Magnetic Resonance Imaging scan (also abbreviated, for the tongue-tied, to M.R.I). Both of which were unusual experiences to say the least, but both were essential to try to locate what part of the brain my seizures were com-ing from.

For the EEG.I had many small disks attached my head with glue, These, in turn, were attached to wires which run to a machine that print-ed out a plot of the electrical activity in my brain on a computer screen. The recorded data was analysed later by the doctors. Any epileptic activity shows up as a large movement of the lines on the screen, rather like an earthquake on a seismograph. This procedure is obviously rather restricting for the patient as he or she is limited by the cables.

Weathering the Storms - living with epilepsy

A variation on this is a 'telemetry test' where the cables are replaced by a radio link. This allows the patient to move relatively freely - they can even sleep - and because of this the test can go on for 24 hours or more, so that much more data can be collected. It also helps that the patient is doing everyday tasks whilst being monitored.

The MRI was a totally different experience. I had to lie down on a sort of conveyor belt, and was slid into a large tube in the centre of what looked like a giant washing machine. This was a noisy experi-

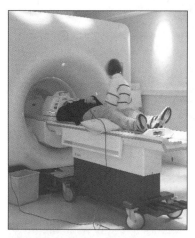

(Left): A Magnetic Resonance Imaging (MRI) scanner and . . .

(Below): . . . some of the brain 'slice' images produced by the MRI scanner

[Photographs: National Society for Epilepsy]

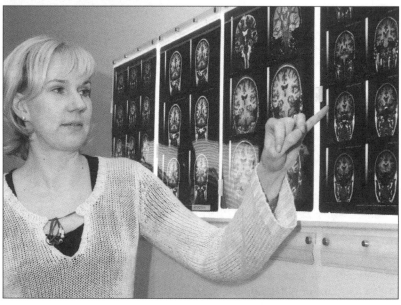

Weathering the Storms - living with epilepsy

The purpose-built assessment facility at the NSE's Chalfont Centre.
[Photograph: David Stewart]

ence - repetitive banging - so I was allowed to use ear plugs. The whole thing lasted an hour and was quite a stressful experience. Magnetic Resonance Imaging uses large rotating magnets - these were what caused the banging noise - to produce colour 'photos' on a computer screen. The images are sections of the inside of the head, as if it had been put through a bacon slicer.

Since I was last an inpatient at the Assessment Unit at Chalfont, a brand new £2.4m unit has been brought into service. The William Gower Centre has a beautiful interior and the latest in technology, and can admit around 300 patients every year. It was built entirely through voluntary donations raised by the National Society for Epilepsy.

I was recently privileged to be given a guided tour of the William Gower Centre. The whole building was obviously designed to be pleasant and spacious. The corridors and communal rooms were decorated with lovely pictures, many of which had a seahorse theme. It was explained that the Latin name for seahorse, hippocampus, was also the part of the brain where common forms of epilepsy arise. There is an emphasis on safety. For instance, the floor is carpeted, there are grab rails lining every corridor and ground level alarms. For those of us who suffer with epilepsy, things like this are important.

At the Centre there are up to 26 patients at one time. Each one is assigned to a named nurse for medical problems. Working alongside the nurses are six key workers who each deal with four or five patients. The staff have a check list that is followed for each patient's care whilst they are in the centre, and to help plan their lives in the outside world.

The William Gower Centre has become the worlds leading medical centre for treating and assessing those with epilepsy. I am almost looking forward to my next stay as a patient!

About a year ago I stayed for a few days at my local general hospital. I had slight paralysis down one side of my body. My left arm and left leg were hanging in a most peculiar fashion and as a result I walked strangely. This terrified me because I didn't know what it was. Although the hospital staff made me comfortable, and were very kind, they seemed unsure of what was causing the trouble. This did not give me much reassurance. Realising that this may be an epilepsy-related problem, they referred me to the National Hospital in London. Straight away the specialist said that a possible cause was a high level of anti-convulsants in my blood stream. The dose was lowered and I gradually got better over a period of two weeks. We are still not absolutely sure whether the pills were at the bottom of this strange incident. The uncertainty was the worst thing about the experience. If I had known what was causing the frightening symptoms, I don't think I would have panicked to the extent that I did.

A more recent stay at the National Hospital involved an EEG. Once again, I had small discs and wires attached to my head, but on this occasion it was slightly different. I was being videotaped throughout the 24-hour test in a specially equipped room. Because of this, I was not allowed to move from my bed. If I wanted to use the toilet, I had to ask for a commode to be brought in, and even that was taped - they assured me that only my head would be in shot! There was a microphone in the room too, to detect any strange noises that I might make.

The test lasted for 24 hours. This was not long, especially as the frequency of my seizures varies from day to day, but it was much longer than a conventional EEG that lasts for no more than an hour.

The nurses were very kind. I was told to press an alarm button every time a seizure occurred so that the staff could check on me. I found I was buzzing every few minutes because I had had an absence. The investigation was particularly concentrated on the morning. For some reason this is my worst time of day. In the mornings I have more seizures than any other time, and I am also very confused. It can take up to two or three hours to recover.

During my entire stay I was in a room on my own. I was afraid that I would get bored and lonely. However, there was a multi-channel television and video player available so I found myself watching the chat shows on cable TV. They always make me laugh so the hours passed quickly. I also had visitors. My best friend came in to bring me some sweets and to chat with me for over an hour. My epilepsy doctor also spent some time with me. We spoke about the tests and any follow-up treatment. We also discussed the writing of this book. He has taken a great interest in my writing over the last few years, and has given me inspiration and encouragement.

I think I may have become a little depressed before going into hospital. Nothing useful had been spotted in my previous EEG tests, and I couldn't help thinking it would be the same again. However, this time I knew that there were many seizures on the recording so I came out of the hospital with a feeling of great hope. I couldn't help smiling to myself as my husband and I walked to catch our train home.

When I went for the follow-up appointment, my doctor told me that the 24-hour test had been useful because many seizures had been seen during the period. This is the first time my seizures have been so fully recorded on an EEG. Perhaps this means that I can look to a better future and some remedy may be found. Only time will tell, but I feel that progress has been made.

As you will realise, someone who frequently falls down is likely to see the inside of a hospital casualty unit from time to time. Occasionally I have been taken there by ambulance with the sirens going following a particularly serious fall. The stays last from a few hours to overnight, depending on the type of injury. I may have concussion, nasty burns or deep cuts.

Typically, my husband takes me to the local hospital which, fortunately has a casualty (more correctly Accident and Emergency) unit. We wait at the desk behind men with bleeding hands and crying children comforted by harassed mothers. We cannot help overhearing their stories of ladder accidents, car crashes and slipped kitchen knives. At last it is our turn to give my details and recount the tale. We are told there is a six hour wait. What! Surely this is a lie intended to put off those who have come with a 'trivial' injury.

After about 15 minutes, the triage nurse calls me for an examination. I go through my story again and she inspects the damage. I am sure she will have put me on a priority list and I will soon be patched up and on my way home again.

Three hours later there is no apparent movement of the queue of unfortunates in the waiting area. I grumble to the nurse that I haven't eaten for eight hours and she kindly finds me a sandwich and some biscuits left over from the staff canteen.

There is a television high on the wall of the waiting area and for much of the time it is ignored. At 8pm, soap opera *Eastenders* comes on and the room is suddenly hushed. A few minutes into the programme, someone unfortunate enough to have been with a doctor at the start whispers a request in my ear for an update. We see living proof of the programme's chart-topping viewing figures. As soon as it is over, the room returns to its former hubbub.

Finally, exactly six hours after we arrived, my name is called. We are shown to a small room packed with alarming looking machines and gadgets. I lie down on the bed and await the doctor. Whilst I wait, the nurse takes my temperature and blood pressure. Eventually I am seen by the doctor - actually a schoolboy masquerading as one, at least that's what he looks like. Like a police suspect, I am obliged to trot out my story yet again, only this time I have to add my life history to persuade the doctor that I haven't been knocked about by my husband. He exits, promising to return shortly.

By this time, we are resigned to the idea of waiting, so the next half hour passes quickly whilst we listen to the groans, cries and screams of our fellow patients. The doctor returns declaring that I have broken my nose and a rib but there's absolutely nothing they can do for me except give me pain killers. I grumpily thank him and we leave, seven and half hours after my fall.

Because of this sort of experience, I tend not to go to hospital if the fall is not a serious one. If there is nothing that can usefully be done for me there really doesn't seem a lot of point in going. If I have a seizure in the street, no matter how trivial, there is often a passer by who wants to call an ambulance. But this is often not the most useful thing to do as I am whisked away for many hours instead of being allowed to spend ten minutes recovering and then getting on with my shopping.

These are just some of the times spent in hospital. I feel that being a patient can be hard work, the many tests and examinations, the waiting and the travelling can put a lot of strain on me. A trip to the hospital in London makes me very tired by the time I get home, and I can even feel quite poorly the next day. My husband says he also feels the strain of these regular trips. Having said that, I could not live my life without hospitals and all they do for me.

20 Some lighter moments

Despite having a serious condition, I find there are lighter times. There are days when a seizure manages to raise a smile.

When I was a child, my absences were very frequent. Even a seizure lasting just a flicker of an eye could produce a situation that was comical or bizarre.

One such situation from those days was when I was playing in the garden on my swing. I loved swinging higher and higher; it was thrilling. As tea-time was approaching, my mother called me to sit down at the table. I was swinging as high as I could, and then decided to jump off. I had a brief blackout and must have carried on what I was doing. As I jumped, I caught my school dress on the hook at the

side of the swing and tore it badly. Needless to say my mother was very angry and gave me a good telling off. I never mentioned what had happened, because I knew I would have jumped anyway - I just might have been a bit more careful if an absence had not occurred.

I got into trouble again, this time when I was in London's Trafalgar Square. Hundreds of pigeons were flying around and I pleaded with my mother to let me buy some seed for the birds. She finally agreed, and I carefully held the seed ready to scatter it. Once again I had a brief absence. Impatient for their feed, the birds flew down and took the seed from my hand and walked all over me. Not only that, in that split second of unconsciousness, the birds managed to deposit their droppings all over me. My school blazer was covered.

Weathering the Storms - living with epilepsy

When I was about thirteen or fourteen, which is a very impression-able age for a girl, I started to notice the opposite sex. And amazing-ly I managed to use epilepsy to my advantage. My chemistry teacher was the only male teacher in an all-girls' school. He also happened to be very nice looking and I had rather a crush on him. Whenever I asked for help I would get it. For instance, he was always helping me with the Bunsen burners to make sure I was safe. When I boasted of this, the older girls got rather annoyed as they thought they deserved more of his attention. I had similar success with the lifeguard at the swimming pool. My mother told me always to tell the lifeguard about my condition before I started swimming. For some reason I have not had a seizure in salt or chlorine water, but I would tell the life-guard anyway to keep an eye on me and to make sure I did not stray into the deep-end of the pool. It gave me the chance to speak to an extremely nice looking young man. I enjoyed every minute. I would feel pleased with myself; after all none of my friends had a good rea-son or excuse to speak to the life guard.

A few years ago, I had a moment that I will never forget because it raises a smile every time I think about it. Whilst visiting Milton Keynes I had a tonic clonic seizure. A short time later, I had recov-ered enough to get into the car, but I decided that I wanted the toi-let. My husband told me to wait for a few minutes, as he could see I was in no fit state to do anything. I must explain here that when I have just come out of a large seizure I tend to be very self-willed and argumentative. I was determined to go to the toilet so we stopped at the nearest public convenience. I went inside, shun-ning all offers of assistance. I looked at all the strange shaped basins on the wall, but did not think anymore about it. I went to the toilet and on emerging from the cubicle I saw several men stand-ing there. I challenged them, suggested that they should have something better to do with their time, and swore at them in no uncertain terms to go away. I got back into the car where my fam-ily was waiting for me, and I told my husband about the strangely equipped room and the horrible men standing inside. My husband explained patiently and as nicely as possible that I had in fact been in the gentlemen's toilet. I felt embarrassed and small, but I have learnt with time that a smile is the only answer. It has been several years since this took place, but even now it raises a smile. What the men must have thought of me I really don't know. To be honest I don't really care. Everyone is entitled to one moment in time where they make complete and utter fools of themselves. I am no different.

Sometimes a seizure can disrupt the lives of those around me. On one occasion my husband and I were on the railway that goes up Mount Snowdon in Wales. The day had gone well, but just as the train was arriving at the foot of the mountain, I had a grand mal seizure and took half an hour to recover. Luckily we were on the last train of the day or we would have had to travel up Snowdon again whilst I regained consciousness. The volunteer workers on the railway did not see themselves as lucky, though, as they had to wait for me to recover before they could move the train into its siding for the night.

I once forced a tourist information centre to close for a period. Whilst my husband and I were looking for leaflets at a motorway services, I collapsed on the floor. The staff were very helpful but they didn't want customers milling around me as I recovered, so they closed the doors to the public for nearly fifteen minutes until I could stand up again.

Occasionally I happen to be in a supermarket when a large seizure happens. A few years ago I collapsed in the checkout aisle, causing the staff to close it. They were very good about allowing me sufficient time to recover. Help and kindness like this does not go un-noticed.

It can be surprising to see how different shops or even members of the public cope with seizures. I once collapsed whilst I was in Marks & Spencer in the town where I live. I was about six feet from the till, but I was surprised by the reaction of the staff. The checkout lady stayed at her till and did not move at all. But within seconds security staff had come to my assistance and taken me to a room to recover. I was told later the till staff had been trained not to leave their positions just in case a collapse had been a diversion prior to a robbery.

The Royal Tournament is something I have always enjoyed. This demonstration of skills by the armed forces was a favourite annual event, whether I watched it on television or attended the show. I had not been to one since I was a child, so it was with some joy that I learned that my husband had been given two tickets through his work. I wondered, however, whether I would be able to sit through the performance, with its loud bangs and fast movement, without having a seizure. This would not only have spoiled my enjoyment, but also that of the people around me, especially if I had made a noise. Fortunately, throughout the Tournament I had been well. After the show we left the huge exhibition centre and with hundreds of others we crossed the road and walked into the crowded entrance of Earl's Court tube station. Here fate caught up with me and I collapsed, causing the throng to step over and round me. A man in uniform took control of the situation - I think he must have been a policeman, but I forget - he contacted the London Transport Police who took responsibility for me. As soon as I was able to walk, we were guided through a labyrinth of passageways to avoid the crowds and put on an almost empty train for home. This VIP treatment meant that I had none of the pressures of fighting my way through the passengers to get a seat on a busy train, and was very much appreciated.

Another example of officials doing exactly what they are trained for occurred when I was at the National Exhibition Centre in Birmingham. I was with my husband whose firm was one of the exhibitors. After the show had closed, whilst we were tidying up, I collapsed. Within minutes the security staff, who must have seen the whole thing on their cameras, came to my rescue and took me on a trolley to a medical room.

Unfortunately, there is a down-side to trained staff as I found out at another show that my husband attended. I had a small seizure lasting about thirty seconds, during which I remained standing, but was conspicuous because it happened in a doorway that dozens of people were trying to get through. This was spotted by a volunteer first aider who very efficiently whisked me off to the first aid room. When I had become coherent again, he asked me several questions so that he could fill in an incident report form. One of the questions was: "Did you lose consciousness at anytime". The reply had to be "yes", but this resulted in the first aider becoming very insistent on calling an ambulance. His rule book told him that anyone who becomes unconscious must be seen by a hospital doctor, and he was going to obey the rules at all costs. It took both my husband and I a great deal of persuasion to avoid having to go to hospital for what was the sort of seizure that I have many times every day. In the end we had to sign a disclaimer to let the over-zealous volunteer off the hook.

Weathering the Storms - living with epilepsy

21   Dreams can come true

Fifteen years after I wrote my diary, my life has changed dramatically and I have achieved many things. The most memorable moments were fulfilling two of my life long ambitions, but more of that later.

When I was in my twenties, there were days when making a cup of coffee or getting downstairs safely would be something to be achieved. These days should not be forgotten. They were indeed bad days. But even throughout the bad times there were good moments.

When I got married and had children it was a difficult time, but the fact that I had two normal, happy children cannot be overstated. All sorts of special arrangements had to be made for them when they were young, and as they got older when they went to school. It wasn't easy, but parenting can be very rewarding and I am proud of the way they have both turned out. My sons have coped with the changes in my epilepsy over the last twenty years; the good days, the not so good days, and the bad days. For safety reasons I did not do all of the motherly duties, but I have always been there for both of them in spirit, and we are now very close.

A few years ago, I attended cookery classes at our local college. My husband and children were thrilled. The other students were all ages and had some kind of disability, such as cerebral palsy or missing limbs. I got on really well with everyone. There was no examination at the end of the course, the idea was to cook different dishes for the fun of it. Because if the safety implications of me having a seizure whilst cooking, I had to bring along a friend to watch me and she also enjoyed herself. I would bring home a different dish each week and my family would always enjoy my fancy creations. Unfortunately, the day of the course changed and my 'minder' was no longer able to take me, so I had to stop going.

Achieving my ambitions were truly wonderful moments.

The first of these was a hot-air balloon flight. Many companies provide such flights for members of the public in groups of a dozen or so. I found a local one and, fingers crossed, told them about my epilepsy. I explained that there was a slight possibility that I might have a seizure, and asked whether this would stop me flying. They said no problem, provided I had someone with me to act as a 'minder'. I asked Paul, who was then aged 15, if he would come with me, and he readily agreed. My husband would follow our path from the car, accompanied by David. When the day came, it was warm and calm, perfect for ballooning. After helping fill the balloon, we took off in the early evening. I was worried in case a seizure did occur, but I only had small absences which did not spoil the enjoyment of my fellow passengers. We had a wonderful time. People on the ground

My husband took lots of pictures of my balloon flight

waved at us, dogs barked, and the view was truly wonderful. The silence was deafening, just the occasional roar from the burner keeping us aloft. As we slowly drifted over Hertfordshire, I was near to tears. The most risky part of the journey was the landing, but I survived that and was able to assist in folding the balloon away at the end. The day finished with the pilot treating us all to a buck's fizz. A truly memorable day.

My second ambition again involved flying. This time at the other extreme - very noisy and rather frightening - a helicopter flight that was a surprise present for me. The whole family was able to fly because we had exclusive use of the aircraft for an hour. After a long wait, we finally took off from a grass airfield near the M25. The flight was much less sedate than the balloon. We ducked and dived all over London, across St. Paul's and the Thames. It was wonderful. The noise was so bad that we had to wear headphones. We wondered if this would cause me to have a seizure, but-nothing happened, although I was very excited indeed. Perhaps it was my determination to enjoy the occasion. In fact, the one who was ill was my husband, who suffered from air sickness!

A still from a video we made of my helicopter trip over London

When I started writing this book, I had one remaining ambition; to visit the Pyramids. My father spent the last years of his life in Cairo and I have always had a deep fascination for the area and its ancient treasures. At last, I am about to achieve this ambition. My husband and I will be celebrating our silver wedding anniversary shortly by touring Egypt.

There are other things I have done that have been particularly satisfying. One was to write this book, something I never thought would be possible. When the idea was suggested to me, I could think of enough information to fill two or three pages, but did not believe there was enough for a whole book. Despite this, and encouraged by friends and family, I had a go. Somehow my life just seemed to pour out, little by little, until eventually I found I had enough information for a book. I jotted this down in a large notebook, but it still wasn't suitable for publication.

One thing was obvious. If I stood any chance of impressing a publisher, I had to turn the book into good English and had to get it onto a computer. The former was easy - my husband worked as an editor - but the second was much more challenging as I hate technical things, especially computers.

For years, I had put off learning how to use a computer, but I was so keen to write this book that with a bit of willpower it all came naturally. I signed up for an evening course at my local college. It was obviously intended for people like me as it was called Computing for the Terrified! This actually meant "computing for those who do not have a clue."

When I attended the first lesson, I found that my twenty fellow students ranged from a young teenage girl to an old man of about 75. Every Tuesday night for several weeks we would all try our best to support each other. Some found it easier than others, and the ones that were fast learners would assist those that did not find it quite so easy. I thought the first lesson was easy as I already knew a little about word-processing, but the course got harder as it went on. Finally, it all sank in, and at the end of the course we all received a certificate. I still have doubts about using a computer, but at least I have the confidence to be able to sit down and tell myself not to panic. Above all, I have been able to fulfil my ambition of writing this book.

As I write this sentence, the book is almost complete and I am both pleased and excited and looking forward to the final stage - finding a sympathetic publisher. In any case, I will always have a document of the past years, which I will be pleased to keep.

When I was very young, I wrote Christmas plays for the children of the family to perform to the adults. Writing has always been a pastime or even a hobby. One day if I get the chance I would like to write a play about disabilities but that is a long way off.

I am proud to say that, despite everything I have managed to live a full and eventful life. My advice for anyone with any disability, but particularly with epilepsy, is to enjoy the moment and above all enjoy life. I have found that with this attitude, I can do the same things as anybody else. Having epilepsy does not make a person second rate, but it has taken my whole life to realise this. It is nothing to hide, nothing to be frightened of, and above all nothing to be ashamed of. So now 46 years into my life, I can hold my head up.

Epilogue:
What if?

What if?

What if we find a cure?
We will one day. Of that I'm sure.
We will be parted after so long,
Years we've seen together. Is this wrong?
Will I miss you? Old friend I call you now.
I think I will, I can't explain how.
Will my family and friends still love me for me?
Bide my time. Just wait and see.
No more black spells, just the light of day.
How strange it will feel in every way.
I know I will miss you but I will be glad
To see the end of an era that was so bad.
So I look forward to saying goodbye,
Even if there is a tear. A moment when I cry.
The brightest days are yet to come,
The happiness, the joy the fun.
So old friend I will draw the line
Under the moments that will be great and fine.
Yes, what if? Oh yes, what if?

Julie Dennison